*W*elcome to Antique Treasures, an indispensable guide for collectors, pickers and sellers of valuable vintage items across Indiana.

In these pages, you'll find information presented in a variety of forms that highlight numerous fun and colorful places across the state to learn about Hoosier heritage and to buy and sell antiques and collectibles.

All parts of Indiana are represented, from the historic Harrison Mansion in Vincennes in the south, to the Kokomo Automotive Museum in the north, to the beloved Riley home in the central region.

Over 450 places are listed, so to help you stay organized, we've separated them into chapters and regions.

In addition to feature stories, listings and business spotlights from antique shops, boutiques and consignment stores, you'll find businesses specializing in auctions, estate appraisals, and restoration. There is even information from historical museums and venues, historical societies and Chambers of Commerce, making the book a virtual visitors guide of our state. It's packed with interesting details about wonderful locations.

We're confident you'll enjoy the book and find it useful as you begin pickin' your way across Indiana.

The Editors at Antique Treasures

ON THE COVER

William Henry Harrison's Grouseland mansion, built in 1803 in Vincennes. It was the first brick house in the Indiana Territory and home to our ninth president when he was the territory's governor.

Introduction

Table of Contents

The Art of Pickin'

By Misty Knisely

> "I do have a little compulsiveness to find neat things at bargain prices."
>
> - Ed Closson

One man's junk just might be another man's junk. But sometimes, it turns out to be treasure. And in many of those cases, there's a picker involved.

Before the small screen pulled them out from behind the curtain, antique pickers were a rare breed known solely by the antique stores they fueled with their finds. Now, as the likes of "American Pickers" and "Pawn Stars" fill the airwaves, it seems everyone is a picker.

But for the ones who were in the game before the game was cool, the hunt for the next great find has been a life-long passion.

Meet Ed Closson.

"Not So Fast Eddie" to anyone who knows him, Closson seems reluctant to call himself a picker.

It's as if he's trying to decide if he's in the game for the business or the love of the hunt for the next great item. The next "peculiar treasure," as he would say.

But there is one thing he does know for certain.

"I'm not a hoarder," he said with a hint of a smile. "But I do have a little compulsiveness to find neat things at bargain prices. I guess that brought the picker out in me."

That drive has filled the room he stands in with thousands of items he's "picked up" over the last 10 years. Walking through the basement of his Logansport antique shop, Fast Eddie's Peculiar Treasures, Closson recalls how he got into the business of picking.

After his brother retired and he found himself running a lumber company alone, he decided to turn his hobby of collecting into a business.

"Some things I've collected for 45 years," he said, rattling off a few favorites while occasionally counting them off on his fingers. "But after my brother retired, I started looking for things that I thought would sell."

He looked for treasures at antique shows, estate sales, auctions and yard sales. At the height of his game in years past — now 70 years old, he's backed off the hunt and focusing more on liquidation — he would hit 15 "or so" in a weekend.

He'll readily admit to making his share of mistakes when he first started.

"There were things I thought looked fancy, but I didn't really know," he said, still wincing years later at the thought of a deal gone wrong.

He learned the hard way what isn't valuable and what won't find a buyer. Like every picker knows, Closson will tell you, you'll win some and you'll lose some. When you win, it's great. A secret to being a good picker is when you lose, you learn something.

Heart's Desire Antique Mall

3030 Old US 20
Elkhart, IN 46514
(574) 294-6096

A "Must See" for the beginner or avid antique collector, Heart's Desire Antique Mall provides a vast selection of beautiful antiques at affordable prices. Specializing in primitives, furniture, shabby chic, plus much more, the mall was selected as one of Michiana's favorite destination locations. There's something for everyone at Heart's Desire. Open year round Tuesday through Saturday, 9 am to 6 pm, Sunday, noon to 5 pm and closed every Monday. Make sure to like their page on Facebook.

Trading Place Antiques

368 South Van Buren Street • Shipshewana, IN 46565 • (260) 768-7090
www.tradingplaceamerica.com

An experience in Amish country wouldn't be complete without shopping for a wide variety of antiques at the Antique Gallery, located just across the street from Shipshewana Auction and Flea Market. Locating hard-to-find items seems like a breeze in their two-story, 31,000 square feet facility that houses over 100 quality antique dealers who carry primitives, jewelry, books, furniture, glassware, pottery, textiles and much more. Stop by and see the wonderful selection for yourself Monday through Saturday, 10 am to 5 pm (October-April) or 9 am to 6 pm (May-September).

Toto Treasures

3115 South Range Road
North Judson, IN 46366
(574) 772-3496

A favorite antique shop in North Judson, Indiana, Toto's Treasures features a wide variety of small and large antiques, candles, rugs and crafts.

The Treasure Chest

18 South Center Street
Flora, IN 46929
(574) 967-3003

Let The Treasure Chest be your one-stop shop for all your antique needs. In addition to appraisals, the business deals in anything from vehicles, furniture, coins, and jewelry to watches and fine art.

Old Creamery Antiques

333 North Main Street
Middlebury, IN 46543
(574) 358-0188

A former creamery turned antique mall, Old Creamery Antiques is packed with kitchen and glassware, fishing gear, coins, automotive memorabilia, furniture, books and collectables.

NORTHERN INDIANA ANTIQUE DIRECTORY

A Wild Hare Antique Mall
401 W Maumee St.
Angola, IN 46703
(260) 665-9920

A1 Upholstery
56787 Shore Ave.
Elkhart, IN 46516
(574) 295-8013

Alley Cat Antiques
310 N Main
Leesburg, IN 46538
(574) 453-2287

Antique Junction
711 Lincolnway
LaPorte, IN 46350
(219) 324-0363
www.malldog.com
Friday-Monday; Summer 7 days

Antiques And More
227 S Main St.
Kendallville, IN 46755
(260) 349-9125

Antiques From Bruce Chaney
10979 N Roanoke Rd.
Roanoke, IN 46783
(260) 672-9744

Antiques On Beardsley
816 W Beardsley Ave.
Elkhart, IN 46514
(574) 523-1955

Antiques on Broadway
1115 Broadway
Fort Wayne, IN 46807
(260) 422-6505
Antique Mall

Antiques On Fifth
109 E 5th St. Suite E
Auburon, IN 46706
(260) 333-0586

Antiques On Main
208 S Main St.
Crown Point, IN 46307
(219) 663-1528
www.antiquesonmaincp.blogspot.com
Historic Downtown Crown Point
Mon – Sat 10am – 5pm, Sun noon-5pm

Antiques On The Square
106 S Main St.
Nappanee, IN 46550
(574) 773-5770
Located in downtown Nappanee

As Time Goes By
614 Lincolnway
LaPorte, IN 46350
(219) 324-4868
Open Wednesday-Friday 10am-5pm;
Saturdays 10am-4pm; Sundays 12noon-4pm

Auburn Select Auctions LLC
122 W 9th St.
Auburn, IN 46706
(260) 402-6080

Auctions America
5536 County Rd. 11A
Auburn, IN 46706
(260) 927-9797

Aunt Nae's Antiques, Gifts, Balloons
302 E. Commercial
Lowell, IN 46356
(219) 690-1180
Downtown Lowell

Auto Michiana Antique Club
448 E 500 S
La Porte, IN 46350
(219) 393-1320

Bailey Gary Auction & Appraisal
7032 N 400 West
Leesburg, IN 46538
(574) 858-2859

Bargain Bin
1002 N Old State Rd. 15
Milford, IN 46542
(574) 527-2176

Bartel & Company Auctions
PO Box 1381
Middlebury, IN 46540
(574) 596-3657

Berne Antique Mall
105 W Water St.
Berne, IN 46711
(260) 589-8050
In Downtown Berne
Open Mon – Sat 10am-5pm

Bernie Payne Auction Service
56314 County Rd. 1
Elkhart, IN 46516
(574) 522-3724

Bill's Rock Shop
113 S Washington St.
Delphi, IN 46923
(765) 564-3073

Billy Sunday Historic Museum
1111 Sunday Lane
Winona Lake, IN 46590
(574) 372-5193

Bireleys Antiques
4577 S US Highway 33
Churubusco, IN 46723
(260) 693-1882

Bixler Upholstery Inc.
21112 County Rd. 40
Goshen, IN 46526
(574) 831-4710

Blue Lakeside Treasures
145 N Morton St.
Shipshewana, IN 46565
(574) 238-6378

Born In A Barn
302 N Heaton St.
Knox, IN 46534
(574) 772-3802
Open Thursday, Friday, Saturday 10am-5pm

C & B Upholstery
514 N Beech Rd.
Osceola, IN 46561
(574) 679-9355

C & J Resale And Antiques
11605 State Rd. 120
Middlebury, IN 46540
(574) 536-1575

Camille's Antiques & Collectibles
115 W Joliet
Crown Point, IN 46307
(219) 662-8780
Downtown Crown Point
Buy – Sell - Trade

Canal Street Gallery
805 E Canal St.
Winona Lake, IN 46590
(574) 371-2777

Candlelight Antiques
3205 Broadway
Fort Wayne, IN 46807
(260) 458-8308
Open Tues. – Sat. 11am-5pm

Canery
1811 Laura Ave.
Kendallville, IN 46755
(260) 343-0180

Center For Traditional Arts
160 Morton St.
Shipshewana, IN 46565
(574) 596-1022

Century Antiques
1011 W Jefferson St.
Plymouth, IN 46563
(574) 936-4783
Jim and Sandy Manuwal, owners.
Established 1969. Open Monday-Saturday
9am-5pm.

CH Upholstery
5367 County Rd. 56
Saint Joe, IN 46785
(260) 337-5127

Charlie's Place Antiques & Junk
400 N Main (US 27)
Geneva, IN 46740
Something for Everyone!

Chupp Auctions & Real Estate
890 South Van Buren St.
Shipshewana, IN 46565
(574) 536-8005

City-County Heritage Museum
25386 County Rd. 32
Goshen, IN 46526
(574) 875-7366

Coachman Antique Mall
500 Lincoln Way
La Porte, IN 46350
(219) 326-5933
Oldest and largest antique mall in Northwest
Indiana. Open Monday-Saturday 10am-5pm;
Sunday 12noon-5pm

Coppes Commons
401 E Market St.
Nappanee, IN 46550
(574) 773-0002

Corner Stone Antiques
122 N Illinois St.
Monticello, IN 47960
(574) 583-0088
Pre-loved furniture from yesterday
re-loved for today.

Cottage Shops Artisan & Antique Mall
2252 NW Shafer Dr.
Monticello, IN 47960
(574) 583-8382
Across from Indiana
Beach Convention Center

Country Copper Polishing
625 US Highway 6
Corunna, IN 46730
(260) 281-2565

Country Side Antiques & Mall
8049 W US Highway 30
Larwill, IN 46764
(260) 327-3050

Countryside Auctions LLC
4505 S 900 W
Topeka, IN 46571
(260) 593-0011

Craig Antiques Appraisals

105 N First St.
Pierceton, IN 46562
(574) 594-2244

Creative Fish Art Gallery

200 E Pickwick Dr.
Syracuse, IN 46567
(574) 457-2789

Crown Point Antique Mall

103 W Joliet St.
Crown Point, IN 46307
(219) 662-1219
www.crownpointantiquemall.com
80 Dealers- 3 Floors of Antiques,
Collectibles and Unique Gifts
Business Hours: Mon- Sat 10am-5pm
Sun noon-5pm

Dealmakers Flea Market

2846 Old US 20 W
Elkhart, IN 46514
(574) 343-2583

Delphi Antique Mall

117 S Washington St.
Delphi, IN 46923
(765) 564-3990

Detroit Street Antique Market

603 Detroit St.
LaPorte, IN 46350
(219) 778-9144
Open Saturdays Only 8am-2pm

Downtown Design & Consign

101 S Main St.
Nappanee, IN 46550
(574) 773-9200

Dragonflies

402 E Commercial
Lowell, IN 46356
(219) 690-1901
Historic Downtown Lowell
Furniture, glassware, pottery,
primitives, home décor, vintage jewelry,
stained glass windows,
1950-1960 retro, art and florals.
Hours: Tue, Wed, Fri & Sat. 10am- 4pm,
Thursday- call first

Duanes Furniture Repair & Upholstery

1212 W Lake St.
Warsaw, IN 46580
(574) 267-2504

Dunfee Plumtickled Junction

5310 S 800 E. 92
Fort Wayne, IN 46818
(260) 625-5082
Located on the Allen/Whitley County line
between 30 & St Rd 14, this antique store is
in an original building built in 1883. They have
a café in back that serves lunch through the
week and breakfast & lunch on Sat.
Open Tues – Sat 10am-5pm

Dutch Village Market

700 N Tomahawk
Nappanee, IN 46550
(574) 773-2828

Early Ford V-8 Museum

2181 General Doolittle Dr.
Auburn, IN 46706
(260) 927-8022

Eastside Resale
115 S 22nd St.
Goshen, IN 46528
(574) 533-1876

Ellis Furniture Restoration
1743 S Main Ln.
Pierceton, IN 46562
(574) 594-3498

Estate Collection
2109 LaPorte Ave.
Valparaiso, IN 46383
(219) 476-0077
www.greatestatecollections.com
This unique shop specializes in vintage and estate jewelry, art, furniture and collectibles.

Family Heirlooms
2985 S Hoosier Hwy.
Bluffton, IN 46714
(260) 824-8965
Open Wed., Thurs. & Fri. 5pm-7pm

Family Tree Antiques
618 Adams St.
Decatur, IN 46733
(260) 728-2880
Open: Mon-Fri 1pm-5pm

Felicia's Antiques And Collectibles
324 E Commercial
Lowell, IN 46356
(219) 696-1221
www.antiquesofnewi.com
Downtown Lowell

Fletcher Upholstery
2315 N Riley Rd.
Columbia City, IN 46725
(260) 248-2020

Fourth Street Emporium
402 Broadway
Chesterton, IN 46304
(219) 728-1238
This cozy emporium specializes in antiques, uniques and consignment. Uncover treasures like vintage clothing, dolls, toys, baseball cards, furniture, jewelry, lamps and china.

Frey's Furniture Stripping And Refinishing
2916 Elkhart Rd.
Goshen, IN 46526
(574) 537-0793

Garrett Auctioneering
1012 E Summitt St.
Wawaka, IN 46794
(260) 318-4034

Getz Bros Auctioneers
413 W Waterford St.
Wakarusa, IN 46573
(574) 286-6558

Goshen Antique Mall Inc.
107 S Main St.
Goshen, IN 46526
(574) 534-6141

Greene's Exit 215 Antique And Artisan Mall
3300 W Clark St.
Rensselaer, IN 47978
(219) 866-5140
www.exit215antiques.com

Handmade Quilts Inc.
975 S Van Buren St.
Shipshewana, IN 46565
(260) 768-7758

Hannah Lindahl Children Museum

1402 S Main St.
Mishawaka, IN 46544
(574) 254-4540

Havilah House

102 W Beardsley Ave.
Elkhart, IN 46514
(574) 266-6596

Heart Of The Lakes Antique Mall

132 N Main St.
North Webster, IN 46555
(574) 834-3000

Heart's Desire Antiques Mall

3030 Old US 20
Elkhart, IN 46514
(574) 294-6096

Heart's Desire, Antiques & Crafts

1040 E Hwy 10
Knox, IN 46534
(574) 806-0581
Open Thursday-Sunday 10am-5pm

Heirloom Appraisals

323 Morton St.
Shipshewana, IN 46565
(260) 336-0387

Home Place Antiques

Hwy 25
Fulton, IN 46931
(574) 201-8503
Wednesday-Saturday 10am-5pm;
Sunday 1pm-5pm

Homestead Antiques

255 N Hetzler Ct.
Angola, IN 46703
(260) 665-3920

Hostetler's Hudson Auto Museum

760 S Van Buren St.
Shipshewana, IN 46565
(260) 768-3021

Howard Surplus Salvage

0200 W Toto Rd.
North Judson, IN 46366
(574) 806-0403

Indiana Antique Company

123 S Buffalo St.
Warsaw, IN 46580
(260) 901-1306

J & S Auctions

68244 State Rd. 13
Millersburg, IN 46526
(574) 642-0444

James Lambert

10452 Vistula Rd.
Osceola, IN 46561
(574) 679-4691

James Madison Furniture, Stripping, Refinishing

28591 Old US 33
Elkhart, IN 46516
(574) 294-3749

JML Enterprises Unlimited Inc.

24120 County Rd. 142
Goshen, IN 46526
(574) 831-6767

Junk And Disorderly Antiques And Resale

203 Broadway, Suite A
Chesterton, IN 46304
(219) 805-7328
www.facebook.com/JunkAndDisorderly/
AntiquesandResale
You never know what you'll find at this shop,
since they get new items in quite often.

Kankakee Valley Auction

9224 S 875 E
Walkerton, IN 46574
(574) 586-9883

Kathy's Antiques

1599 S. Calumet Rd.
Chesterton, IN 46304
(219) 926-1400
An upscale dealer of fine antiques and
jewelry. They've got a licensed appraiser
on staff if you have questions about
particular items.

Katie's Antiques
219 S Calumet Rd.
Chesterton, IN 46304
(219) 926-5559
This antiquing destination, housed in a historic mansion, features room upon room of items like fine furniture, porcelain and ivory.

Keeper Of The Past
20672 4B Rd.
Walkerton, IN 46574
(574) 586-9086

Kuhns Upholstery
115 Plymouth Goshen Trl.
Nappanee, IN 46550
(574) 773-2928

Leather Or Knot Antiques
222 E Market St.
Logansport, IN 46947
(574) 722-3931

Lillypad Antiques
3466 S County Rd. 210
Bass Lake, IN 46532
(574) 772-3466
Open Thursday-Sunday
10am-5pm (CST).
Antiques and vintage treasures.

Linda's Treasure Trove
1816 Wells St.
Delphi, IN 46923
(765) 564-3649

Locust Hill Antiques
204 W 3rd St.
Brookston, IN 47923
(765) 563-1000

Main Street Mall Antiques
127 N Main St.
Monticello, IN 47960
(574) 583-2998
Used furniture, collectibles

Marc T. Nielsen Interiors And Antique Shop
734 Old Suman Rd.
Valparaiso, IN 46383
(219)462-9812
www.marctnielseninteriors.com
In a huge Tudor-style barn, you'll find antiques from many cultures, including Asian and European items, art, one-of-a-kind light fixtures and lamps.

Markle Antique Mall
250 E South St.
Markle, IN 46770
(260) 758-2038
Exit 86 off of 69 N on 224

Martin's Quilt Shop
25387 County Rd. 46
Nappanee, IN 46550
(574) 831-2256

Mast Upholstering Inc.
26206 County Rd. 50
Nappanee, IN 46550
(574) 773-4714

McGrew Tractor Parts, Inc.
19828 U.S. Highway 6
New Paris, IN 46553
(574) 831-5800

Menno-Hof
510 S Van Buren St.
Shipshewana, IN 46565
(260) 768-4117

Middlebury Historical Society Inc.
301 W Bristol Ave. (CR8)
Middlebury, IN 46540
(574) 825-0978

Minnich's Antiques & General Store
1123 Otto St.
Uniondale, IN 46791
(260) 227-6056
www.minnichsantiques.com
Give your home décor a makeover with
quality antiques, collectibles & gifts!
Just off St. Rd. 224

Natmus Inc.
1000 Gordon M Buehrig Pl.
Auburn, IN 46706
(260) 925-9100

Nature's Corner Antiques
2307 Spy Run Ave.
Fort Wayne, IN 46805
(260) 486-5236
Open Mon-Fri 10am-6pm

Near East
12423 Michigan Rd.
Plymouth, IN 46563
(574) 897-2766
Antiques, rehab pieces and many other
specialty items.

Nick's Nacks
601 N Main St.
Fulton, IN 46931
(574) 857-2051
Coca-Cola antique specialist.
Tuesday-Friday 10am-6pm

O'Gara And Wilson Ltd. Antiquarian Booksellers
223 Broadway
Chesterton, IN 46304
(219) 728-1326
www.ogaraandwilson.com
This downtown shop buys and sells used
books, and also deals in book-related
collectibles and antiques, autographs,
artwork and photographs.

Old Bag Factory
1100 N Chicago Ave.
Goshen, IN 46528
(574) 238-2791

Old Creamery Antiques
333 N Main St.
Middlebury, IN 46543
(574) 358-0188

Old Farm House Antiques
409 S Main St.
Hebron, IN 46341
(219) 996-5329
This charming store on Hebron's Main Street
contains distinctive furniture, clocks, glassware,
flow blue, pottery, primitives, china, vintage
clothing, collectibles and gifts.

Old Green Shutters Antiques
118 S Main St.
Crown Point, IN 46307
(219) 663-4425
Downtown Crown Point
Email at old.green@comcast.net

Old House Antiques
6156 Fail Rd.
La Porte, IN 46350
(219) 778-2245
Country place filled with
kitchenware, furniture and others.
Visit us by chance or appointment.

Olde Crow Primitives
210 W. 2nd St. (US 24)
Burnettsville, IN 47926
(574) 826-2100
facebook.com/oldecrowprimitives
Country home décor and antiques.

On The Square Antique Emporium
116 S Main St.
Crown Point, IN 46307
(219) 663-3311
Downtown Crown Point
Email at Onthesquareemporium@gmail.com

Parker Antiques
101 N 7th St.
Garrett, IN 46738
(260) 357-4558

Plain & Fancy Antiques
5395 W Johnson Rd.
La Porte, IN 46350
(219) 362-5277

Plymouth House Antiques
523 N Michigan St.
Plymouth, IN 46563
(574) 936-3650

Polk Auction Company LLC
72435 State Rd. 15
New Paris, IN 46553
(574) 831-5100

Praa Auction Center
13861 County Rd. 4
Bristol, IN 46507
(574) 825-4900

Primitive Country
10400 US 35 S
Walton, IN 46994
(765) 461-7727
facebook.com/Primitive-Country
All about Crafts and Primitives! We are
getting new items in weekly! Just N. of
Galveston, IN on US 35!

Rebecca Haarer Arts & Antiques
165 Morton St.
Shipshewana, IN 46565
(260) 768-4787

Rivich Antiques
8737 White Oak Ave.
Munster, IN 46321
(219) 765-8219
www.rivichauction@comcast.net

Roberta's Antiques & Collectibles
117 N First St.
Pierceton, IN 46562
(574) 594-2081

Route 20 Antiques LLC
275 W US Highway 20
Lagrange, IN 46761
(260) 463-0359

Ruby's Cottage Antiques
1816 N. Wells St.
Delphi, IN 46923
(765) 564-3649

Russ & Barbs Antiques
222 W Lincoln Ave.
Chesterton, IN 46304
(219) 926-4937
Stop in and find unique jewelry, art, pottery,
fine china and decorative glass of all styles.

Ruthmere Foundation Inc.
302 E Beardsley Ave.
Elkhart, IN 46514
(574) 264-0330

S & L Woodcraft and Caning
6505 S 500 W
Topeka, IN 46571
(260) 593-0325 ext 1

Shipshewana Area Historical Society
760 S Van Buren St.
Shipshewana, IN 46565
(260) 768-3030

Shop on the Corner
427-B S Calumet Rd.
Chesterton, IN 46304
(219) 250-2087
www.facebook.com/ShopOnTheCorner
Shoppers will find an ever-changing selection of
antiques, collectibles, resale and home décor.

Souders Furniture, Repair, Refinishing
8809 Hanauer Rd.
Fort Wayne, IN 46818
(260) 341-0848

South Bend Regional Museum Of Art
120 S Saint Joseph St.
South Bend, IN 46601
(574) 235-9102

South Side Collectables Antiques And Bike Shop
733 S Main St.
Monticello, IN 47960
(219) 207-1004
www.southsidebikeshop.com
New and used bikes, parts,
repair shop, rentals.

Stoller's Antique Mall
909 N Coliseum Blvd.
Fort Wayne, IN 46805
(260) 422-8527
Open Mon-Fri 10am-6pm

Studebaker National Museum
201 Chapin St.
South Bend, IN 46601
(574) 235-9714

Sweet Violets Tea & Antiques
503 W Wayne St.
Fort Wayne, IN 46802
(260) 426-4832
Open Wed – Sat 11am-4pm

Sydow's Antiques
103 N First St.
Pierceton, IN 46562
(574) 594-9100

Syracuse-Wawasee Historical Museum
1013 N Long Dr.
Syracuse, IN 46567
(574) 457-3599

Tanglewood Restoration
15162 County Rd. 18
Middlebury, IN 46540
(574) 825-1072

The Antique Market
3707 NE Frontage Rd.
Michigan City, IN 46360
(219) 879-4084
www.theantiquemarketmc.com
Open Monday-Saturday 10am-5pm;
Sunday 12noon-5pm

The Cannery
1811 Laura Ave.
Kendallville, IN 46755
(260) 343-0180

The Cluttered Cupboard
10151 US Route 12
Michigan City, IN 46360
(773) 517-1031
Open Saturdays 10am-5pm or by chance

The Copper Butterfly
120 S Main St.
Crown Point, IN 46307
(219) 663-1506
Downtown Crown Point
Check us out on Facebook
Antiques-Unique Gifts and Boutique

The eState
3101 Willowcreek Rd.
Portage, IN 46368
(219) 764-4316
If you're looking for high-end
collectibles, WWII and Civil War
memorabilia, pottery, crystal
or jewelry – this is your destination.
The friendly and professional staff
also repairs jewelry and buys gold.

The Gathering House
105 W Main St.
Berne, IN 46711
(260) 589-8466
Stay and enjoy lunch in this
quaint café in downtown Berne
after browsing their numerous
antiques!

The Little Red Hen House
125 Morton St.
Shipshewana, IN 46565
(260) 499-0554

The Marketplace Of Middlebury
511 S Main
Middlebury, IN 46540
(574) 825-4001

The Trading Post
523 E Jefferson St.
Plymouth, IN 46563
(574) 935-5460
www.thetradingpostplymouth.net
Open Tuesday, Thursday, Friday 11am-6pm;
Saturday 9am-5pm

The Treasure Chest
18 S Center St.
Flora, IN 46929
(574) 967-3003

The Wood Shack
444 W Baker
Fort Wayne, IN 46805
(260) 424-2093
Open Mon., Thurs., Fri., &
Sat. 10am-5pm

Then & Now Antique Mall Inc
200 W Maumee St.
Angola, IN 46703
(260) 665-6650

Times Past Antiques & Collectables
215 S Washington St.
Delphi, IN 46923
(765) 564-6317

Tish's Antiques
201 E Commercial Ave.
Lowell, IN 46356
(219) 690-1666
www.antiquessofnwi.com
Downtown @ the tracks in Historic Lowell
Est. 1975

Toto Treasures
3115 S Range Rd.
North Judson, IN 46366
(574) 772-3496

Trading Place
368 S. Van Buren St.
Shipshewana, IN 46565
(260) 768-7090

Turquoise-N-Treasures
400 W Fisher St.
Monticello, IN 47960
(574) 583-8143
www.turquoisentreasures.com
Indian jewelry, swords, brass & copper,
antiques.

Uniquely Made
160 N Morton St.
Shipshewana, IN 46565
(260) 367-1612

Up Towne Shoppes
623 State St.
LaPorte, IN 46350
(219) 325-3929
Open Monday, Wednesday, Thursday,
Friday 10am-5pm; Saturday 10am-4pm;
Sunday 10am-4pm

Village Antique Gallerie
109 N First St.
Pierceton, IN 46562
(574) 594-9494

Walkerton Area Historical Society
413 Michigan St.
Walkerton, IN 46574
(574) 586-3868

Yesterday's Treasures
700 Broadway
Chesterton, IN 46304
(219) 926-2268
With more than 100 dealers
and two floors of treasures,
this is definitely the area's
largest and most eclectic
antique mall. You'll find items
in all price ranges — and if you're
looking to do consignment or sell
an estate, they can help you
with that, too.

Yesteryears Antiques & Collectables
525 E Market St.
Logansport, IN 46947
(574) 753-7371

Yvonne Marie's Antique Mall & Collectables
152 S 2nd St.
Decatur, IN 46733
(260) 724-2001
www.facebook.com/yvonnemariesantiquemall
Specializing in Antique Furniture!
Open Mon – Sat 10am-5pm
Sun 1pm – 5pm
1st Sun of every month 10am-5pm

Central Indiana Antiques

The best antiques are old friends.

Historic National Yard Sale

By Carson Gerber

"That's the beauty of it. It's the spontaneity. You never know what you're going to find."

- Patricia McDaniel

There's a road running through central Indiana that on most days is just like any other highway in the state. Long, straight stretches sail through seas of corn, occasionally passing through small towns and a big city.

But once a year, the highway transforms into something truly unique — an 854-mile stretch of heaven on earth for antique enthusiasts and deal hunters.

Since 2006, the Historic National Road Yard Sale has turned U.S. 40 from St. Louis to Baltimore into the nation's longest and biggest rummage sale. In Indiana, the road runs from Richmond, through Indianapolis, to Terre Haute.

Thousands of antique stores, second-hand shops and local residents set up along the roadway, offering deals on just about anything under the sun.

Food, clothes, cars, furniture, antiques, historic memorabilia, even puppies — it's all for sale

for five days along U.S 40. The event always takes place the first Wednesday after Memorial Day and runs through Sunday.

"If it's legal, it's for sale," said Patricia McDaniel, who first came up with the idea for the event and still organizes it every year. She's the owner of an antique shop called The Old Storefront in Dublin, Ind., which sells antiques, vintage pharmaceuticals and movie props.

For serious antique hunters, McDaniel said the sale offers one of the best and most concentrated opportunities to find some real gems at sometimes amazing prices.

But a word of advice: To find the best deals and the rarest items, you'll need to get out on the road early. You won't be alone out there, cruising along the highway.

"It's bumper-to-bumper traffic," McDaniel said. "The diehard antiquers are really out in force, especially early in the week. But

if you're willing to get up at the crack of dawn, you really do find some treasurers."

For antique enthusiasts, McDaniel said the best places in Indiana to find that one-of-a-kind item along the route are Centerville, Knightstown and Lewisville.

But, she said, you never know where you'll come across that special something that catches your eye.

"That's the beauty of it," McDaniel said. "It's the spontaneity. You never know what you're going to find."

The sale is about more than just finding a good deal, though. McDaniel said she first organized the event as a special way to celebrate the bicentennial of America's oldest superhighway.

Centerville Antique Mall

200 W. Union Street • Centerville, IN 47330 • (765) 855-5551

Located on I-65 at the 76B exit, in Edinburgh, Indiana, the Exit 76 Antique Mall is a great place to browse and shop for those unusual and hard-to-find items or unique gifts. It features 600 booths and lighted cases, full of everything from antiques and collectible to modern artisan creations. It is truly a collector's dream!

Yesterday's Antiques

20 West Main Street • Cambridge City, IN 47327 • (765) 478-9371

Stroll back in time as you walk through the halls of Vinton House, home to Yesterday's Antiques in Cambridge City, Indiana. Built in 1947, the three-story federal brick hotel provides the perfect ambiance for both the casual shopper and seasoned antique finder. Enjoy two floors of early American and country primitives from 13 different dealers. Whether looking for furniture, glassware or "purposeful clutter", Yesterday's Antiques in the place to be. For those interested in the history of antiques, the shop even hosts a museum. Take a trip through history and enjoy this wonderful shop and all it has to offer. Open Tuesday through Saturday 10 am to 5 pm and Sunday noon to 4 pm.

Pizzazz Antiques, Homegoods & Gifts

225 East South Street. • Lebanon, IN 46052 • (765) 484-8739
www.pizzazzantiques.com

Enter a world of forgotten elegance at Pizzazz Antiques, Homegoods and Gifts. Located in a beautiful 1890's Queen Anne home, the delightful shop offers a variety of different items including antiques, furniture, stained glass, lamps, accent décor, linens, rugs, pottery and jewelry. Choose from their wide selection of china and glassware featuring such classics as Noritake and Haviland Limoges. And while you're at it, check out the large variety of coffee and tea and many accessories. Even their resident dog Duchess adds an undeniable charm to any visit. Stop by Tuesday through Saturday 10 am to 5 pm or Sunday noon to 4 pm.

The Old Shed

3522 South 500 West • Russiaville, IN 46979 • (765) 883-8323
www.theoldshed.com

Have you been looking everywhere for that perfect piece of antique furniture? Search no further than The Old Shed in Russiaville, Indiana. For more than a decade, the shop has been known for their unique and exceptional pieces of 18th and 19th American country, traditional and primitive furniture with accessories. They also host one of the finest antiques shows in the Midwest, The Pure and Simple show, held always on the first Saturday in May. Check out their website at www. theoldshed.com to see photographs of some of the unique items they have to offer.

Marketplace Antiques

413 North Washington Street • Kokomo, IN 46901 • (765) 450-5624
www.facebook.com/marketplacekokomo

Having a difficult time locating a hard-to-find or highly desirable item? Chances are Marketplace Antiques will have it. Located in historic Kokomo, the shop specializes in truly unique antique, vintage and collectable items. While their regular inventory includes industrial, décor, gas/oil, toys, primitives, glass and much, much more, new objects are acquired daily. Stop by Monday thru Saturday from 10 am until 6 pm and discover a little hidden treasure of your own at a price that's hard to beat.

Countryside Antique Mall

4889 North U.S. Highway 52
Thorntown, IN 46071
(765) 436-7200

Whether you're searching for beautiful cut glass or a piece of Civil War history, Countryside Antique Mall and its 10,000 square feet of displays will satisfy most any need. Conveniently located just five minutes from I-65, the 23-year-old business features an amazing variety of antique furniture, glassware, primitives and collectables.

Hometown Treasures

223 West Washington Street
Lebanon, IN 46052
(765) 481-2400
Email: hometown223@live.net

Situated in a refurbished gas station, Hometown Treasures sells a little bit of just about everything. With a large variety of vendors, the shop offers a charming assortment of antiques, collectables, paintings by artist, glassware, jewelry, china, furniture, silver, as well as other vintage items. Chances are if you stop by for a look, you won't be going home empty handed. The store is open 10 am to 5 pm Wednesday through Saturday and noon to 5 pm on Sundays.

2nd Chance
Resale Shop
845 Indianapolis Avenue
Lebanon, IN 46052
(765) 336-2286

www.facebook.com/2ndChanceResaleShop

Opening their doors on September 1, 2013, 2nd Chance Resale Shop offers a large shopping selection including antiques and vintage items, new and used modern décor, costume jewelry, DVDs, music, seasonal pieces, tools and much, much more. Owners Amy and Bryan know the value of your hard earned dollars and have made it their goal to sell quality merchandise at an affordable price.

Mo's Vintiques
319 West Main Street
Lebanon, IN 46052
(765) 481-2133
www.mo'svintiques.com

Mo's Vintiques sells transportation and vintage racing items in a charming 1920's gas station. You can also find literature and vintage advertising to complete your collection. Tucked inside is The Powder Room dedicated to vintage dressing room collectables. Take home a bar of locally-made soap or old-fashioned candy before you leave.

CENTRAL INDIANA ANTIQUE DIRECTORY

2nd Chance Resale Shop
845 Indianapolis Ave.
Lebanon, IN 46052
(765) 336-2286
www.facebook.com/2ndChanceResaleShop

2nd Time Around
1776 Hannibal St.
Noblesville, IN 46060
(317) 776-0877

A-1 Turner Restoration
232 E Main St.
Plainfield, IN 46168
(317) 627-5343

Abbotts Antiques
191 Rapid Rill Ln.
Brownsburg, IN 46112
(317) 858-0910

Absolute Antiques
102 W Main St.
Lewisville, IN 47352
(765) 478-4809

Action Auction
8935 Covington Blvd.
Fishers, IN 46037
(317) 845-9454

Angel Blue Antiques
30 S 9th St.
Noblesville, IN 46060
(317) 674-8338

Antique At Comtekcom Inc.
101 S Main St.
Fairmount, IN 46928
(765) 948-5550

Antique Emporium Group Shop
1055 S Rangeline Rd.
Carmel, IN 46032
(317) 844-8351

Antique Mall
8112 Talliho Dr.
Indianapolis, IN 46256
(317) 849-6169

Antiques & More
3440 N Shadeland Ave.
Indianapolis, IN 46226
(317) 542-8526

Antiques On Square
5732 Michigan Rd.
Indianapolis, IN 46228
(317) 916-8125

Artsplash Gallery
111 E Main St.
Westfield, IN 46074
(317) 564-4834

Auction And Flea Market
2311 N Lynhurst Dr.
Indianapolis, IN 46224
(317) 484-8002

Audrey's Place Inc
3228 E 10th St.
Indianapolis, IN 46201
(317) 266-1644

Aunt Patty's On The Square
101 W High St.
Rockville, IN 47872
(765) 569-7442

Aunty's Antiques
5501 E Washington St.
Indianapolis, IN 46219
(317) 322-1970

B&D Auction Exchange LLC
3484 Sedgemoor Cir.
Carmel, IN 46032
(317) 873-1756

Back Through Time Antique Mall
9 W Main St.
Rossville, IN 46065
(765) 379-3299

Baxter Auction Gallery
8051 E 46th St. Suite 1X
Indianapolis, IN 46226
(317) 542-0026

Bittersweet Memories
121 E Main St.
Knightstown, IN 46148
(765) 345-7480

Bloomin' Barn Antiques
6424 N US 41
Bloomingdale, IN 47832
(765) 597-2096

Brown Bear Auction Company LLC
23478 US 31
Cicero, IN 46034
(317) 752-0622

Brown's Antiques
315 N 5th St.
Zionsville, IN 46077
(317) 873-2284

Buckland & Assoc
19205 Amber Way
Noblesville, IN 46060
(317) 770-1517

Burroughs Upholstery & Antiques
150 E 46th St.
Indianapolis, IN 46205
(317) 931-1336

Cabbage & Kings Antique Mall
124 S Washington St.
Crawfordsville, IN 47933
(765) 362-2577

Caldwell's Antiques & Flea Market
5600 N Wheeling
Muncie, IN 47304
(765) 289-5555

Carmel Custom Refinishing
4275 W 96th St.
Indianapolis, IN 46268
(317) 872-3999

Carmel Old Town Antique Mall
38 W Main St.
Carmel, IN 46032
(317) 566-1908

Centerville Antique Mall
200 W Union St.
Centerville, IN 47330
(765) 855-5551

Certified Prompt Appraisal
51 Glasgow Ln.
Noblesville, IN 46060
(317) 776-0109

Chaudion On Site Gallery Auction
22690 State Rd. 19
Cicero, IN 46034
(317) 984-9200

Chez De La Joyeuse
1232 Willow Way
Noblesville, IN 46062
(925) 634-1637

Chitwood Auctions
2775 W 150 S
Lebanon, IN 46052
(765) 482-3528

Christy's Of Indiana LLC
6851 Madison Ave.
Indianapolis, IN 46227
(317) 784-0000

Clowes Memorial Hall Of Butler University
4602 Sunset Ave.
Indianapolis, IN 46208
(317) 940-9603

Cochrans Antiques
4255 S Lynhurst Dr.
Indianapolis, IN 46221
(317) 856-6089

Countryside Antique Mall
4889 N. U.S. Hwy. 52
Thorntown, IN 46071
(765) 436-7200

Danville Trading Post
170 Old Farm Rd.
Danville, IN 46122
(317) 745-5737

Deja Vu
1060 E Main St.
Brownsburg, IN 46112
(317) 858-1961

Devine Antiques
2141 S 4th St.
Lafayette, IN 47905
(765) 588-6291

Dishman Upholstery Shop
1213 N Gale St.
Indianapolis, IN 46201
(317) 636-3307

Domont Studio Gallery
545 S East St.
Indianapolis, IN 46225
(317) 685-9634

Dorman Auctions
5685 Trammel Ct.
Carmel, IN 46033
(317) 460-9889

Doublehead Trading Company
133 W Main St.
Cambridge City, IN 47327
(765) 478-3800

Dusty Rusty Stuff
7 W Main St.
Cambridge City, IN 47327
(765) 478-9300

E B Ball Center
400 W Minnetrista Blvd.
Muncie, IN 47303
(765) 285-8975

Earls Auction Co. Inc.
5199 Lafayette Rd.
Indianapolis, IN 46254
(317) 291-5843

Eckert Fine Art Galleries Inc.
5627 N Illinois St.
Indianapolis, IN 46208
(317) 255-4561

Eiteljorg Museum
12759 Brookshire Pkwy.
Carmel, IN 46033
(317) 752-9590

Eiteljorg Museum Of American
500 W Washington St.
Indianapolis, IN 46204
(317) 636-9378

Emporium Flea Market
3535 S Emerson Ave.
Beech Grove, IN 46107
(317) 787-1865

Enflora Gallery
111 Monument Cir. Suite 140
Indianapolis, IN 46204
(317) 686-0290

Evan Lurie Gallery Inc
30 W Main St. Suite 1000
Carmel, IN 46032
(317) 844-8400

Fairmount Antique Mall
101 S. Main St.
Fairmount, IN 46928
(765) 948-5550
Same location for the past 20 years!

Fancy Fat Antiques
3504 Walton Way
Kokomo, IN 46902
(765) 453-6361

Firehouse Antique Mall
85 E Cedar St.
Zionsville, IN 46077
(317) 733-1073

First Class Clutter
638 Main St.
Lafayette , IN 47901
(765) 429-5758

Fivethirty Resale, LLC
20 N Main St.
Zionsville, IN 46077
(317) 567-7781

Fosters E Street Gallery
825 N E St. 829
Richmond, IN 47374
(765) 935-9055

Fox In Box Antiques
3478 S 575 E
Whitestown, IN 46075
(317) 769-6649

Frost Upholstery Shop Inc
4024 E Michigan St.
Indianapolis, IN 46201
(317) 353-1217

Furniture Conservatory
2052 E 46th St.
Indianapolis, IN 46205
(317) 253-0876

Furniture Doctor
10845 Golf View Dr.
Indianapolis, IN 46234
(317) 852-6427

Gallery On Square
51 S Washington St.
Danville, IN 46122
(317) 386-3111

Garden Gate Gift & Flower Shop
107 W Pearl St.
North Salem, IN 46165
(765) 676-5039

Gilley's Antique Mall
5789 E U.S. Hwy. 40
Plainfield , IN 46168
(317) 839-8779

Gizmos Galleria
1630 E Northfield Dr.
Brownsburg, IN 46112
(317) 350-2399

Glass Cupboard
115 E Main St.
Knightstown, IN 46148
(765) 345-7572

Goose Heaven Trading Co.
16320 Goose Heaven Rd.
Cambridge City, IN 47327
(765) 478-3020

Hamilton County Art Center
195 S 5th St.
Noblesville, IN 46060
(317) 776-2278

Hardy's Auction Service & Real Estate
11812 Southeastern Ave.
Indianapolis, IN 46259
(317) 862-2381

Harris Auctions
226 S Brookfield Dr.
Lafayette, IN 47905
(317) 509-2138

Heimel Auction Service Inc.
59 N 2nd Ave.
Beech Grove, IN 46107
(317) 783-9627

High Hats At The Depot Antique Mall
417 N 8th St.
Richmond, IN 47374
(765) 994-0050

Hole In The Wall Antiques
131 W Main St.
Cambridge City, IN 47327
(765) 478-6363

Hometown Treasures
223 W Washington St.
Lebanon, IN 46052
(765) 481-2400
Email: hometown223@live.net

Hoosier Antiques
1431 Broad St.
New Castle, IN 47362
(765) 529-2105

Hoosier Auction Co
251 N Illinois St. Suite 180
Indianapolis, IN 46204
(317) 917-1794

Hoosier Gold Buyer LLC
5038 Kentucky Ave.
Indianapolis, IN 46221
(317) 830-8025

Hot House Market
900 Kossuth Ave.
Lafayette, IN 47909
(765) 490-7968

Indiana Historical Society
555 Kessler Blvd W Dr.
Indianapolis, IN 46228
(317) 253-7137

Indiana Historical Society Inc
450 W Ohio St.
Indianapolis, IN 46202
(317) 232-1882

Indiana Medical History Museum
3045 W Vermont St.
Indianapolis, IN 46222
(317) 635-7329

Indianapolis Museum Art Inc.
4000 Michigan Rd.
Indianapolis, IN 46208
(317) 923-1331

Indianapolis Museum Contemporary Art
1043 Virginia Ave. Suite 5
Indianapolis, IN 46203
(317) 634-6622

Indy Auctions LLC
2612 Millgate Ct.
Carmel, IN 46033
(317) 507-4797

Irvington Flea Market Inc.
6301 E Washington St.
Indianapolis, IN 46219
(317) 375-1885

Irvington Historical Society
5350 University Ave.
Indianapolis, IN 46219
(317) 353-2662

J.E. Field Co.
634 Main St.
Lafayette, IN 47901
(765) 742-6500
jefieldco.com
J.E Field Co. specializes in custom furniture, lighting, art and unique accessories.

J.W. Riley's Emporium
107 W Main St.
Greenfield, IN 46140
(317) 462-5268

Jake's Antiques Etc.
1440 W Winona Ave.
Marion, IN 46952
(765) 664-9765
Furniture, glassware, toys and more.

John Wilson Commadore
3744 N Lesley Ave.
Indianapolis, IN 46218
(317) 545-2423

Kasnak Restorations Inc.
5505 N County Rd. 1000 E
Brownsburg, IN 46112
(317) 852-9770

King Appraisal Services Inc.
136 S 9th St. Suite 324
Noblesville, IN 46060
(317) 776-9490

Klassy Klutter Antiques
2135 S 4th St.
Lafayette , IN 46905
(765) 838-2738

Kurt Vonnegut Memorial Lib Inc.
340 N Senate Ave.
Indianapolis, IN 46204
(317) 423-0391

La Rose Antique Mall
124 W Main St.
Crawfordsville, IN 47933
(765) 362-1707

Lake & Lodge Outfitters
610 E Main St.
Arcadia, IN 46030
(317) 984-7555

Leaping Leopard Antiques
2145 S 4th St.
Colburn, IN 47905
(765) 474-9100

Magdalena Gallery Of Arts
27 E Main St. Suite 100
Carmel, IN 46032
(317) 844-0005

Main Street Antiques & Collectibles
915 S Main St.
Kokomo, IN 46901
(765) 457-4333

Main Street Mercantile
1502 Cason St.
Lafayette, IN 47904
(765) 742-1520

Marketplace Antiques
413 N Washington
Kokomo, IN 46901
(317) 331-1957

Matt Gardner Homestead Museum
6036 E 43rd St.
Indianapolis, IN 46226
(317) 547-9386

Memory Lane Antiques
125 W Jefferson St.
Tipton, IN 46072
(765) 675-3004
www.facebook.com/memorylaneantiques
Glassware, Furniture, Linens & More
Something for Everyone!

Mickey's Autograph Arena Inc.
1950 E Greyhound Pass Suite 18
Carmel, IN 46033
(317) 818-7706

Midland Arts & Antiques Market
907 E Michigan St.
Indianapolis, IN 46202
(317) 267-9005

Mo's Vintiques
319 W Main St.
Lebanon, IN 46052
(765) 481-2133
www.mo'svintiques.com

Mockingbird Antiques
107 S Morton Ave.
Centerville, IN 47330
(765) 277-3577

Museum Interaction Inc.
12626 Royce Ct.
Carmel, IN 46033
(317) 843-2761

Museum Of Miniature Houses And Other Collections Inc.

111 E Main St.
Carmel, IN 46032
(317) 575-9466

National Council On Public History

425 University Blvd.
Indianapolis, IN 46202
(317) 274-2716

National Road Antique Mall

39 W Main St.
Cambridge City, IN 47327
(765) 478-9070

National Trail Antique Mall

113 Washington St.
Dunreith, IN 47337
(765) 987-6057

Neva's Antiques And Collectibles

120 W Ohio St.
Rockville, IN 47872
(765) 569-3644

New Beginnings Consignments

211 W Main St.
Plainfield, IN 46168
(317) 443-4084

North Salem Antiques & Sundries

15 W Pearl St.
North Salem, IN 46165
(765) 894-6638

North-Wind Antiques

1020 E Sycamore St.
Kokomo, IN 46901
(765) 236-0996

Ohrberg Refinishing Services

8625 Jamaica Ct.
Indianapolis, IN 46219
(317) 895-8481

Old Storefront Antiques

1837 Main St.
Dublin, IN 47335
(765) 478-4809

Onsite Woodwright LLC

912 E Epler Ave.
Indianapolis, IN 46227
(317) 840-9733

Outta The Shed LLC

71 S Washington St.
Danville, IN 46122
(317) 518-4249

Over The Back Fence

52 Main St.
Frankfort, IN 46041
(765) 654-0200

overthebackfence.net

Pastfinder Antiques

1005 Churchman Ave.
Beech Grove, IN 46107
(317) 783-7161

Percussive Arts Society

110 W Washington St. Suite A
Indianapolis, IN 46204
(317) 974-4488

Pizzazz Antiques, Homegoods & Gifts

225 E South St.
Lebanon, IN 46052
(765) 484-8739
www.pizzazzantiques.com

Plunder On The Square

51 N Jackson St.
Frankfort, IN. 46041
(765) 659-3262

Post Road Funiture Inc.

4601 N Post Rd.
Indianapolis, IN 46226
(317) 897-2889

Pour House Antiques & Sweets

109 W Main St.
Cambridge City, IN 47327
(765) 478-4000

Purciful Upholstery & Machine Quilting
28445 Lamong Rd.
Sheridan, IN 46069
(317) 758-4263

R Beauchamp Antiques Inc
16405 Westfield Blvd.
Westfield, IN 46074
(317) 896-3717

RamZ's
205 Farabee Dr. N
Lafayette, IN 47905
(765) 448-9104

Raven's Roost Antiques
2200 Elmwood Ave. Suite B-1
Lafayette, IN 47904
(765) 588-6449

RDC Inc
800 E Main St.
Westfield, IN 46074
(317) 867-3327

Red Barn Antique & Flea Market
325 E 106th St.
Indianapolis, IN 46280
(317) 846-8928

Red Ribbon Antiques
101 W Main St.
Greenfield, IN 46140
(317) 462-5211

Richard Fee Auctioneer
10102 Plumtree Dr.
Indianapolis, IN 46235
(317) 823-2170

Riley Memorial Association
528 Lockerbie St.
Indianapolis, IN 46202
(317) 631-5885

Roseburgh Upholstery Inc.
3325 N Dequincy St.
Indianapolis, IN 46218
(317) 546-3728

Ruma Upholstery & Draperies
4337 W 96th St. Suite 400
Indianapolis, IN 46268
(317) 872-7862

Scott Worley's Upholstery
5137 Norwaldo Ave.
Indianapolis, IN 46205
(317) 257-1011

Scowden's Antiques
14 S 3rd St.
Lafayette, IN 47901
(765) 589-3093

Serendipity Antiques
3730 Coventry Way
Carmel, IN 46033
(317) 844-3455

Shadeland Antique Mall

3444 N Shadeland Ave.
Indianapolis, IN 46226
(317) 546-2402

Shoup House

100 N Winans St.
Battle Ground, IN 47920
(765) 567-4132
shouphouseantiques.com
1860s Italianate - Federal style home with 11 rooms of antiques to explore.

Silk Purse Antiques

76 S Main St.
Zionsville, IN 46077
(317) 732-0025

Simple Thyme Antiques & Primitives

50 W Clinton St.
Frankfort, IN 46041
(765) 652-2504

Smith Village Stripper

914 3rd Ave. SW
Carmel, IN 46032
(317) 844-6069

Solomon Antique Restoration

1105 E 52nd St.
Indianapolis, IN 46205
(317) 466-0586

Southport Antique Mall Inc.

2028 E Southport Rd. Suite A
Indianapolis, IN 46227
(317) 786-8246

Sowers Upholstery

1811 Cicero Rd.
Noblesville, IN 46060
(317) 773-2988

Stone Station Antiques

10421 Hillsdale Dr.
Carmel, IN 46032
(317) 332-0593

Strawtown Auction Barn

22217 State Rd. 37 N
Noblesville, IN 46060
(317) 773-5590

Studio Black Antiques

404 S Washington
Kokomo, IN 46901
(765) 457-3373

Sully's
406 Main St.
Lafayette, IN 47901
(765) 250-5142
facebook.com/sullyssullyssullys
Men's & women's curated
vintage clothing, lingerie, jewelry,
art, gifts, pretty
stuff and nice things!

Summit Auction Group
6747 Kentland Cir.
Indianapolis, IN 46237
(260) 403-4235

Swayzee Antique Mall
115 N Washington St.
Swayzee, IN 46986
(765) 922-7903
Buying Estates
Open Mon., Wed., Thurs. 10am-5pm
Fri. & Sat. 10am-6pm, Sun. Noon-6pm,
Closed Tues.

Taylor Center Natural History
12308 Strawtown Ave.
Noblesville, IN 46060
(317) 984-5556

Ted Deane Upholstery
9 N 18th Ave.
Beech Grove, IN 46107
(317) 783-5117

Teien Keith Interprises Incor
11795 Pursel Ln.
Carmel, IN 46033
(317) 571-1633

Tenth & Cherry Galleria
215 S 10th St.
Noblesville, IN 46060
(317) 776-7880

The Black Crow
662 Main St.
Lafayette, IN 47901
(765) 420-0563

The Enchanted Sleigh
410 E Main St.
Centerville, IN 47330
(765) 855-2567

The Log House Antiques
124 W Main St.
Cambridge City, IN 47327
(765) 334-8268

The Old Shed
3522 S 500 W
Russiaville, IN 46979
(765) 883-8323
theoldshed.com
Quality furniture and Primitives

The Olde Brass Hog
124 N Morton Ave.
Centerville, IN 47330
(765) 967-0889

The Original Treasure Mart
1201 E Vaile Ave.
Kokomo, IN 46901
(765) 459-3148

The Red Rooster
1001 W Main St.
Greenfield, IN 46140
(317) 462-0655

The Stripping Workshop
8336 N 1050 W
Colfax, IN 46035
(765) 324-2172
www.thestrippingworkshop.net

Thompson Upholstery
603 W Mill St.
Danville, IN 46122
(317) 745-5901

Total Recall Antiques
8 E Main St.
Brownsburg, IN 46112
(317) 852-0050

Trader Buck's Flea Market
190 Old Farm Rd.
Danville, IN 46122
(317) 745-1500

Treasure Mart Mall
116 W Alto Rd.
Kokomo, IN 46902
(765) 455-9855
treasuremartantiques.com
Over 70 Dealers all located
under one roof with 25,000 sq. ft.
of fine antiques and
collectibles.

Treasures, Antiques & Collectibles
713 King St.
Pershing, IN 47370
(765) 478-5000

Tru-Finds Treasures
931 Indianapolis Ave.
Lebanon, IN 46052
(765) 484-8339

Turkey Hill Farm Antiques and Uniques
7498 N Marshall
Marshall, IN 47859
(765) 597-2000

Turkey Run Furniture And Antiques
10636 N Henley Rd.
Marshall, IN 47859
(765) 597-1914

Turner Refinishing
232 E Main St.
Plainfield, IN 46168
(317) 839-5836

Upscale Junk And Antiques
23478 US 31
Cicero, IN 46034
(317) 801-0200
www.upscalejunkandantiques.com
Buy, Sell, Consign Find Us On Facebook

Vendor City Flea Market
537 S Reed Rd.
Kokomo, IN 46901
(765) 450-7374

Wallen Ridge
National Road
Dublin, IN 47335
(765) 322-0020

War Memorials Commission Ind.
431 N Meridian St.
Indianapolis, IN 46204
(317) 232-7615

Wheeler's Antiques
106 & 107 W Main St.
Centerville, IN 47330
(765) 855-3400

White River Architectural Salvage
100 W Main St.
Centerville, IN 47330
(765) 855-1908

White Truck Auction Co. LLC
3984 Chadwick Dr.
Carmel, IN 46033
(317) 580-1629

Wickliff Associate Auctioneers
12232 Hancock St.
Carmel, IN 46032
(317) 844-7253

Wild Ostrich
928 S Main St.
Kokomo, IN 46901
(317) 452-3990
facebook.com/Wild-Ostrich-Antiques
Open Thurs., Fri. and Saturdays 10- 5

Wild Wood Country
210 W Elizabeth St.
Greencastle, IN 46135
(765) 653-0033

Yankee Peddler Antiques
1929 Tanglewood Dr.
Lafayette, IN 47905
(765) 448-6274

Yesterday's Antiques
20 W Main St.
Cambridge City, IN 47327
(765) 478-9371

Yesterday's Treasures
973 S Meridian St.
Portland, IN 47371
(260) 726-8175

Country Elegance

Southern Indiana
Antiques

Shakers Landing Antiques

1238 South 18th Street • Vincennes, IN 47591 • (812) 886-6024

www.shakerslandingantiquemall.com

In 2006, Joyce and Larry Phegley opened Shakers Landing, a 10,000 square foot building of uniqueness and artistic display. Before visitors even get to the front door, they are greeted with 5,000 square feet of outside displays, larger outdoor antiques and architectural salvage.

Joyce and Larry take pride in having unusual and historical items. Any visit to Shakers Landing creatively entices a person to travel through history.

Not only does Shakers Landing provide a vast, eclectic array of antiques, they also offer custom framing and antique restoration services.

Ever-changing, Shakers Landing is constantly expanding. Come take a stroll through THE antique place to shop in Southwest Indiana. Open Monday through Friday, 10 am to 5 pm; Saturday, 10 am to 5 pm and Sunday, noon to 5:00 pm.

White River Valley Antique Show
Located at Daviess County Fairgrounds
West Indian St. at Whisman St. • Elnora, IN 47529 • (812) 636-4847

White River Valley Antique Show is held annually starting the first Thursday after Labor Day.

Located in Elnora, Ind., which is about two hours from Indianapolis, Terre Haute, Evansville and Louisville.

Plan to bring the family and enjoy four full days of all kinds of Antique Farm machinery, demonstrations & displays, a huge flea market, great food and free parking. There is something for everyone to see and do !

For additional information, please visit our website: http://www.wrvaa.org/

Worthington Antiques
206 East Main Street • Worthington, IN 47471 • (812) 384-2879

Worthington Antiques is located on the northside of the triangle in historic downtown Worthington, Indiana. The 3,000 square foot shop is full of original finish antique cupboards and early wares. Along with the antiques, the store carries hand-loomed coverlets, blankets and rugs. Make Worthington your next weekend destination.

Exit 76 Antique Mall

12595 North Executive Drive • Edinburgh, IN 47124 • (812) 526-7676
www.exit76antiques.com

Located on I-65 at the 76B exit, in Edinburgh, Indiana, the Exit 76 Antique Mall is a great place to browse and shop for those unusual and hard-to-find items or unique gifts. It features 600 booths and lighted cases, full of everything from antiques and collectible to modern artisan creations. It is truly a collector's dream!

Historic Bloomington Antique Mall

311 W. 7th Street • Bloomington, IN 47404 • (812) 323-7676

Located in downtown Bloomington, in one of Indiana's most vibrant historical districts! There is so much to see in the area, and the Bloomington Antique Mall is at the heart of it! Visitors can shop for the unusual and unique in antiques, artwork, artisan-made crafts and more! You never know what special treasure you may find.

Whimsy

3189 South 3rd Place • Terre Haute, IN 47802 • (812) 686-2893

From the light-hearted lady to the fanciful princess who loves her frills, the unique clothing boutique Whimsy will enchant every visitor. Representing everything that is feminine and fun, the shop carries everything from sassy, flowing tops and dresses to smart tutus for the little ones. Accessorize that funky style with the latest in fashion trend jewelry. Like their Facebook page and see all their forward fashion firsthand. Open Tuesday through Friday from 11 am to 5 pm and Saturday, 10 am until 3 pm.

Peddler's Corner

1420 H. Street • Bedford, IN 47421 • (812) 278-3192

Peddler's Corner opened in 1998 and was recently remodeled in 2013. We pride ourselves in providing affordable antiques, collectibles, primitives, country home décor and primitive furniture. We also offer a great collection of glassware. Thurs-Sat 1-5, Sunday 1-5. Other days and times by appointment.

Main Street Gifts

74 N Main Street
Linton, IN 47441
(812) 847-3215

At Main Street Gifts you can check out over 4,000 square feet of your favorite candles and scents, gifts for all occasions, collectibles, primitives, textiles and home decor items, works by local artists, fashion accessories and MORE. Our friendly knowledgeable staff is waiting to welcome you.

Morton Avenue Antique Mall

619 Morton Avenue
Martinsville, IN 46151
(765) 352-8477

With 5,000 square feet and 40 booths, Morton Avenue Antique Mall provides visitors with a friendly atmosphere while they shop from a wide selection of antiques, primitives, cabin/lodge and home décor in Martinsville. Conveniently located 30 miles south of Indianapolis and 20 miles north of Bloomington, Indiana's premier antique mall is open seven days a week. Come in and find your very own special treasure.

The Blue Door Old Timers Group LLC

at the Gasthof
Montgomery, IN 47558
(812) 259-9605

Rapidly becoming one of the tri-state's most popular antiques and collectibles store, The Blue Door in Montgomery, IN carries a wide variety of exceptional items. The collection at the Blue Door is eclectic, ranging from fine glassware to primitives, vintage jewelry, cast iron, and much more. Located in Southern Indiana, the store strives to provide a fun, relaxing and peaceful shopping experience to all its guests.

Monday-Saturday 11am-7pm; Sunday 11am-4pm

Words & Images/ The Train Place

19040 Main Street
Metamora, IN 47030
(765) 647-1212
www.metamoralanterns.com

Words & Images/ The Train Place specializes in kerosene lighting, cast iron cookware, and toy train and railroad items.

Aunt Arties Antique Mall

128 West MainStreet
New Albany, IN 47150

The Antique Mall is housed in a Civil War Hospital historic building. We have over 35 dealers selling antiques & collectibles, jewelry, quilts, paintings, books, dolls, crocks and much more. Hours M-S 10-5 /Sunday 1-5

Pulskamp Auto Body and Restoration

2100 South County Road 700 East
Greensburg, IN 47240
(812) 663-7769

Located in Greensburg, Pulskamp Auto Body and Restoration has specialized in classic and antique auto body repair for 40 years.

SOUTHERN INDIANA ANTIQUE DIRECTORY

American & European Antiques
706 N Main St.
Evansville, IN 47711
(812) 421-1720

Angels In Attic Antique Consignments
5040 Bellemeade Ave.
Evansville, IN 47715
(812) 475-2811

Antique Americana
3307 W Maryland St.
Evansville, IN 47720
(812) 421-9685

Antique Emporium
525 Church St.
New Harmony, IN 47631
(812) 682-3407
30 plus dealers with furniture,
glassware, jewelry, quilts, Civil War
memorabilia and more.

Antique Shak
204 Main St.
Gentryville, IN 47537
(812) 937-2533
Sundays 12pm-4pm
or Call for an appointment

Antique Store
246 E Walnut St.
North Vernon, IN 47265
(812) 346-8995

Antiques Attic
145 E Market St.
New Albany, IN 47150
(812) 941-0437
HRS: TUES.-SAT. 11-5
Closed Sunday & Monday

Anything Collectible
1295 W 1100 S
Ferdinand, IN 47532
(812) 367-1559

Aunt Arties Antique Mall
128 W. Main St.
New Albany, IN
(812) 945-9494
Hrs: Mon. – Sat. 11-5

Awesome Finds And Collectibles LLC
2211 State St.
Columbus, IN 47201
(812) 372-1775

B & B Antiques & Collectibles
108 W 2nd St.
Mount Vernon, IN 47620
(812) 838-5598

Back In Thyme
408 4th St.
Huntingburg, IN 47542
(812) 354-4799
Collectibles, Primitives, Antiques and Toys.

Blacksmith Antiques & Primitives
12 N Main St.
Linton, IN 47441
(812) 847-0998

Blessinger Collectibles LLC
807 Soliga St.
Jasper, IN 47546
(812) 481-1393

Blue River Valley Antique
4631 N 330 W
Columbus, IN 47201
(812) 376-0290

Bott Antiques
10 E National Ave.
Brazil, IN 47834
(812) 448-2891

Broadway Antiques
219 N Broadway St.
Seymour, IN 47274
(812) 522-9538

Brown County Antiques Mall
3288 State Rd. 46 E
Nashville, IN 47448
(812) 988-1025

Brown's Antiques
1230 Union St.
Columbus, IN 47201
(812) 375-6797

Buds Uncle Antiques
12115 N State Rd. 129
Batesville, IN 47006
(812) 934-4627

C & C Antiques
6390 E County Rd 400 S
Greensburg, IN 47240
(812) 663-5842

Car Von S Antique Heirlooms
12520 Browning Rd.
Evansville, IN 47725
(812) 867-5831

Carolyn's Collectibles
22 N Old Michigan Rd.
Holton, IN 47023
(812) 689-5180
Antiques, furniture, lamps, dishes, pictures, nic-nacs, primitives. Open Sunday, Monday, Thursday, Friday and Saturday 10-5. Closed Tuesday and Wednesday.

Carriage House Antiques
3038 Pearl St.
Oldenburg, IN 47036
(812) 932-2090
carriagehouseoldenbu.wit.com

Charlie James Antiques
204 Main St.
Evansville, IN 47708
(812) 423-7415

Chic & Tiques
512 Main St.
New Harmony, IN 47631
(812) 682-3352
www.chic-tiques.com
Enjoy the historic ambience of an 1800's store front while shopping an impressive collection of Native American, art deco, and other better quality antique jewelry.

Cloverland Beehive
6472 W State Rd. 340
Brazil, IN 47934
(812) 240-2181

Cooper Plaza Antiques & Collectibles
118 Cooper St.
Loogootee, IN 47553
(812) 295-5533

Country Cousins
285 S Gardner St.
Scottsburg, IN 47170
(812) 752-6353
Antiques, Collectibles, Fiestaware, Stone Ware

Days Gone By Antiques
2 W McClain Ave.
Scottsburg, IN 47170
(812) 752-9355
Antiques, Collectibles & Misc Merchandise

Diana's Antiques
4244 W Base Rd.
Switz City, IN 47465
(812) 659-3871

Dogwood Acres Antiques & Auction
11905 State Rd. 46
Sunman, IN 47041
(812) 623-7028

Edward Creek Antiques
707 N Main St.
Evansville, IN 47711
(812) 402-2710
Antiques, Coins, Sterling Jewelry and Post Cards

Elizabeth's Keepsakes Collectibles
237 N Main St.
Rushville, IN 46173
(765) 938-3071

Emporium 31
11 Declaration Dr.
Greenwood, IN 46143
(317) 865-1865

Ewing Antiques
1050 W Spring St.
Brownstown, IN 47220
(812) 358-2666

Exit 76 Antique Mall
12595 N Executive Dr.
Edinburgh, IN 47124
(812) 526-7676

Ferdinand Antique Emporium
1440 Main St.
Ferdinand, IN 47532
(812) 367-1331
12,000 square feet, 53 vendors, you won't be disappointed!

Firehouse Antiques
608 S Main St.
New Harmony, IN 47631
(812) 682-4811
www.facebook.com/firehouseantiques
Closed Tuesday, call ahead if traveling Located in a 1899 Firehouse, we specialize in American furniture, primitives, vintage collectibles and quilts. We do estate tag sales and consignments.

Forever Antiques LLC
709 S Willow Rd.
Evansville, IN 47714
(812) 475-0251

Gold-N-Treasures
222 E Main St.
Madison, IN 47250
(812) 265-5116
Gold & Silver Jewelry, Coins, Antiques, Primitives. Buy-Sell-Trade. Jewelry Repair, Watch Batteries.

Grainry Antiques & Other Needful Things
415 E 4th St.
Huntingburg, IN 47542
(812) 683-0234
www.grainryantiques.com
Grainry Antiques & Other Needful Things has a wonderful selection of antique and vintage glassware, enamelware, graniteware, and pottery.

Home Accents and Antiques
9712 State Route 37
Bedford, IN 47421
(812) 278-6669

Home Town Antiques
621 W Main St.
Mitchell, IN 47446
(812) 849-6487

It's The Berry's
6445 W State Rd. 340
Brazil, IN 47834
(812) 448-8250

J & J Antiques Inc
200 Mount Ashley Rd.
Evansville, IN 47711
(812) 867-1192

Kaleidoscope Treasures
240 N Main St.
Rushville, IN 46173
(765) 969-0412

Little Golden Fox
402 Broadway St.
Madison, IN 47250
(812) 227-4108

Lumber Mill Antique Mall
721 W 1st St.
Madison, IN 47250
(812) 273-3040

Ma Nancy's Antiques
609 W Main St.
Mitchell, IN 47446
(812) 849-2203

Main St. Antiques
615 W Main St.
Mitchell, IN 47446
(812) 849-0625

Main St. Gifts
74 N Main St.
Linton, IN 47441
(812) 847-3215

Marvels Street Marvels
301 S Main St.
Princeton, IN 47670
(812) 386-7212

Mccord Auctions & Consignments
5414 E Morgan Ave.
Evansville, IN 47715
(812) 402-3000

Medieval Collectibles
1501 S 350 E
Princeton, IN 47670
(812) 386-7047

Montgomery Antique Mall
Corner of 1st Street and
Orleans Road
Montgomery, IN 47558
(812) 486-2982

Mooresville Open Market Antiques
5 E Main St.
Mooresville, IN 46158
(317) 584-5814

Morton Avenue Antique Mall
619 Morton Ave.
Martinsville, IN 46151
(765) 352-8477

Mr. Ed's Fudge & Vintage Collectibles
Duck Creek Crossing
Metamora, IN 47030
(812) 212-0096

Mulberry House Antiques
307 Bank St.
New Albany, 47150
(812) 948-1739
Hrs. Tues.-Sat. 11-5

Nancy & Joes Hidden Treasures
104 S 3rd St.
Boonville, IN 47601
(812) 897-8757

North Vernon Antique Mall
5125 N County Rd. 350 W
North Vernon, IN 47265
(812) 346-8604

Now And Then Antiques
3014 Fairlawn Dr.
Columbus, IN 47203
(812) 379-4518

Old Buggy Antiques and Collectibles
1801 Plaza Dr.
Bedford, IN 47421
(812) 583-7843

Old Town Store
110 S Mulberry St.
Corydon, IN 47112
(812) 267-4101

Ole Country Woodshop
743 S State Rd. 61
Winslow, IN 47598
(812) 789-8421
www.olecountrywoodshop.com
Offering old and new furnishings,
collectibles and accessories.
We have wonderful quality antiques from
primitive to early painted
pieces, walnut, cherry, poplar, and oak.
We are always looking for the
antique or collectible you would
like for your home.

Owen Valley Antique Flea Market
2101 State Hwy. 43
Spencer, IN 47460
(812) 828-9006

Paulas Antique & Collectibles
6201 Upton Rd.
Mount Vernon, IN 47620
(812) 838-5730

Peddler's Corner
1420 H. St.
Bedford, IN 47421
(812) 278-3192

Persimmon Tree
213 Main St.
Rising Sun, IN 47040
(812) 438-2800
A century-old drug store with
a blend of antique and collectibles.
Open 5 days per week, 11-4.
Closed Wednesday and Sunday

Petersburg Antiques
Main St.
Peterburg, IN 47567
(812) 486-8647 or (812) 698-1986
Crafts, Refinish, Refurbish, Repurpose.

Picker's Paradise
1810 E 25th St.
Columbus, IN 47201
(812) 378-2121

Pickers Paradise
E. 4th St.
Huntingburg, IN 47542
(812) 684-0110
Check us out on Facebook!
Unique store full of neat items!!

Plum Creek Antiques LLC
3993 Plum Creek Rd.
Nashville, IN 47448
(812) 988-6268

Princeton Antique Mall
115 W Broadway St.
Princeton, IN 47670
(812) 385-1045

Pulskamp Auto Body and Restoration
2100 S County Rd. 700 E
Greensburg, IN 47240
(812) 663-7769

Pump House Antiques LLC
1007 Belgium Blvd.
Bargersville, IN 46106
(317) 292-5338

Queen Anne's Lace
689 S Main St.
Martinsville, IN 46151
(765) 610-0348

Red Barn Antique Mall
215 Highway 62
Corydon, IN 47112
(812) 738-6000

Red Dog Antiques
4355 Stonegarden Ln.
Newburgh, IN 47630
(812) 853-8984

Red Kettle Antiques
8378 N 800 W
Carthage, IN 46115
(765) 565-6067

Remember When Antiques
311 N Broadway St.
Seymour, IN 47274
(812) 522-5099

Renslow's Bargain Barn
925 Indiana 356
Scottsburg, IN 47170
(812) 752-4585
Antiques, Collectibles,
Used Furniture, Misc.

Restoration Innovations
1110 Eisenhower Ave.
Jasper, IN 47546
(812) 481-9967

Riley's Antiques and Gifts
8737 N US 421
Napoleon, IN 47034
(812) 852-3325
Antiques, gifts, candles, purses and country
décor. Open Monday, Thursday and
Friday, 105; Saturday 10-2. Tuesday and
Wednesday by appointment.

River Bluff Antiques
5386 Old Highway 41 N
Patoka, IN 47666
(812) 779-2601
We buy and sell antiques. Glassware,
Advertising, Collectibles, Linens, Decoys,
Pottery, Furniture, Tools, Vintage
Clothing, and Oil Lamps.

River West Antique Mall
1029 W 2nd St.
Madison, IN 47250
(812) 265-0740

Riverside Antique Mall
1205 E Riverside Dr.
Evansville, IN 47714
(812) 469-2255
11,000 square feet of great antiques.
Primitives and home furnishings.
We carry Howard products.

Riverwalk Antiques
124 Main St.
Vincennes, IN 47591
(812) 886-4475

Robert C Brown
18516 E Redbud Ct.
Hope, IN 47246
(812) 546-1100

Ron S Antiques
5406 Rosebowl Ln.
Evansville, IN 47720
(812) 473-4584

Shaker's Landing Antiques

1238 S 18th St.
Vincennes, IN 47591
(812) 886-6024
Monday-Saturday 10am-5pm & Sunday 12noon-5pm.
www.shakerslandingantiquemall.com
Primitives, Vintage Signs, Furniture, Mantles, Doors, Toys, Porch Posts, Windows, Antique & Historical Maps, Coal Mine Relics, Military Relics, and Custom Picture Framing.
Buy, Sell, Trade.

Shady Lane Antique Mall

9247 US 41 S
Terre Haute, IN 47802
(812) 299-1625

Somewhere in Thyme

2234 State Rd. 54 E
Linton , IN 47441
(812) 798-6227

Star Flea Market

2630 Anthony Dr.
Evansville, IN 47711
(812) 477-2517

Step Back In Time Antiques

123 E Main Cross St.
Edinburgh, IN 46124
(812) 526-5409

Strawberry Patch

49 N Main St.
Linton, IN 47441
(812) 699-1144

Stuff and Things

U.S. 40 East
Brazil, IN 47834
(812) 878-5767

Sugar Bucket Antiques

106 S Main St.
Brownstown, IN 47220
(812) 358-2341

Sugar Maples

109 W. Main St.
Jeffersonville, IN 47130
(812) 285-1616

Taylor Antiques
3260 Lonesome Pine Dr.
Nashville, IN 47448
(812) 988-4016

The Antique Market
211 SE 4th St.
Evansville, IN 47713
(812) 426-0210

The Antique Showrooms in the Mews
531 Church St.
New Harmony, IN 47631
(812) 682-3490
Four buildings full of antique furniture, primitives, home décor and new apparel.

The Blue Door at the Gasthof
6747 E Gasthof Village Rd.
Montgomery, IN 47558
(812) 486-3994
Monday-Saturday 11am-7pm & Sunday 11am-4pm
Vintage Glassware, Antique Furniture, Collectibles, Retro & Vintage Items.

The Glass House Antiques
5th and Eastern Ave.
Connersville, IN 47331
(765) 825-3571

The Vault General Store
170 W Washington St.
Morgantown , IN 46160
(317) 506-8197

The Warehosue
426 College Ave.
Bloomington, IN 47403
(812) 350-3451

This & That Flea Market
760 W Morgan St.
Martinsville, IN 46151
(765) 349-2878

This N That Antiques
44 Teke Burton Dr.
Mitchell, IN 47446
(812) 849-4507

Tim Cosper Antiques
P O BOX 83
Riley, IN 47871
(812) 325-5086

Tim S Antiques
204 Main St.
Gentryville, IN 47537
(812) 937-2533

TLC Coins & Collectibles
101 N Fulton Ave.
Evansville, IN 47710
(812) 402-2212

Traderbakers
748 Jefferson Ct.
Madison, IN 47250
(812) 265-9494

Treasure Chest Antiques
421 E 4th St.
Huntingburg, IN 47542
(812) 630-6082
We have a great selection of Antiques, Primitives, and Eclectic Treasures.

Treasures Antique Mall
1104 S. Green River Rd.
Washington Square Mall
Evansville, IN 47715
(812) 473-2988
Check us out on Facebook.
Over 24,000 square feet of antiques and collectibles.

Tremont Antiques
608 SE 2nd St.
Evansville, IN 47713
(812) 426-9099

Uncle Bud's Antiques
12115 N State Rd. 129
Batesville, IN 47006
(812) 934-4627

Vic's Antiques and Uniques
11490 N US 31
Edinburgh, IN 47124
(812) 526-2000

Victorian Parlour Antique Mall

7270 E State Rd. 7
Columbus, IN 47203
(812) 376-0260

Walnut Hollow Antique

19945 E County Rd. 410 N
Hope, IN 47246
(812) 546-1315

Weekend Treasures

2 S State Rd. 145
Birdseye, IN 47513
(812) 389-2105

Westbury Antique Market

3106 Cantebury Court
Bloomington, IN 47403
(812) 333-7601

Whimsy

3189 S 3rd Pl.
Terre Haute, IN 47802
(812) 686-2893

White River Valley Antique Show

Daviess County Fairgrounds
Elnora, IN 47529
(812) 636-4847

Williams Group

615 W Main St.
Mitchell, IN 47446
(812) 849-5505

Words & Images

19040 Main St.
Metamora, IN 47030
(765) 647-1212
www.metamoralanterns.com
Specializing in kerosene lighting,
cast iron cookware, toy train and railroad
items. Open Sat & Sun year round.
Located on the Whitewater Canal in the
center of the historic village
of Metamora. Chimneys and globes
for lamps and lanterns and parts
for restoration and repair available.

Worthington Antiques

206 E Main St.
Worthington, IN 47471
(812) 384-2879

Ye Olde Homeplace

40 S. Main St.
Scottsburg, IN 47170
(812) 752-0100
Primitives, Antiques,
Collectible, Unique Gifts

Yellow Moon Antique Mall

8 W Main St.
Mooresville, IN 46158
(317) 831-8599

Yester Year Antique Shop

1108 State St. 257
Washington, IN 47501
(812) 254-1506
Large selection of fine glassware,
antiques and clocks.

Auctions, Estates,
Appraisals and
Restoration

Dinky's Auction Center

9084 East 550 North • Montgomery, IN 47558 • (812) 486-2880
www.dinkysauctioncenter.com

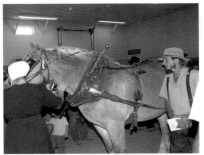

Every Friday night, the 36,000 square foot main building of Dinky's Auction Center fills to capacity with sights and sounds of eight to 10 auctioneers selling anything you could possibly imagine all at one time. The facility is located on the Odon-Cannelburg Road (CR 900 E) just five and a half miles north of Highway 50 in Daviess County.

For many, Dinky's Auction Center represents an unusual entertainment spot to start the weekend. Thousands of people from hundreds of miles around converge in the heart of Amish country to soak in the unique atmosphere and find real bargains.

Consignments are accepted all day Friday while the auction begins as 6 pm. One can buy just about anything including furniture, hand tools, antiques, food, produce, household items, hay, and others items too numerous to mention. Just to attend and take it all in is an unforgettable experience.

In addition to the Friday night auctions, many miscellaneous antique, livestock, horse and pony, tack, carriage, and consignment auctions are held at Dinky's on a regular basis. In fact only one of the Southern Indiana Draft Horse, Carriage, Machinery and Antique Auctions that Dinky's puts on twice a year can draw crowds of 3,000 to 4,000 people. Sellers at these auctions have in the past represented 27 different states and even a few foreign countries.

Are you interested in looking for a peek at upcoming sales? Check out their current list of auctions at www.dinkysauctioncenter.com or www.auctionzip.com.

A Class Act Auction/Products Without Delay

P.O. Box 725 • Plainfield, IN 46168 • (317) 495-8482
www.aclassactauction.com • Sandra Flippin, Auctioneer Lic # AU11300035

When it comes to vintage and antique items, A Class Act Auction/Products Without Delay knows how to deliver integrity, protection and value. We provide a top-notch full service auction company as well as we are one of the #1 rated E-Bay stores for vintage and antique items with a large repeat customer base from around the world. A Class Act Auction will take in your consignments and sell them directly to a targeted market. Many of our consignment includes many different collectible items: i.e. coins, toys, advertising signage, china, glassware and much more. Visit their website at www.aclassactauction.com.

Chupp Auctions & Real Estate

890 South Van Buren Street
Shipshewana, IN 46565
(574) 536-8005

With 20 years of experience in the auction business, Chupp Auctions has become known for their auctioneering and marketing in selling all kinds of items including advertising signs, farm primitives, salesman samples, petroleum items, butter churns and more. The auction business consists of four Chupp brothers working together with several other employees. Located one mile south of Shipshewana, Indiana, Chupp Auction Center and its many sales can be followed on www.auctionzip.com.
(Auctioneer ID #11841.)

Beckort Auctions, LLC

117 ½ E. Chestnut Street
Corydon, IN 47112
(812) 738-9476
www.beckortauctions.com

A Marknet Alliance Member.
Auctioneer and Real Estate Broker.
Licensed in Indiana and Kentucky.

Larry's World

622 F S. Rangeline Road
Carmel, IN 46032
(317) 564-4266
www.motoxtoys.com

Since 1975, this unique shop offers customers the opportunity to buy collectables, used furniture and motorcycles. This business also serves as an Ebay drop off point and consignment store.

Bill's Clockworks

8 West Columbia Street
Flora, IN 46929
(574) 967-4709
www.Billsclockworks.com

Since 1991, Bill's Clockworks has been the go-to-shop for clocks in Central Indiana. With a lifelong love of clocks, owner Bill Stoddard repairs all varieties including 400 day anniversary clocks and those special antique American, French and German clocks. All estimates for clock repair are free. Clocks, such as new Hermle wall and mantel clocks, Kit-Cat clocks and cuckoo clocks, are also available for sale as well as a few antiques clocks. Come and see Bill's vintage Westclox alarm clock display.

Tanglewood Restoration

15162 County Road 18
Middlebury, IN 46540
(574) 825-1072

Specializing in restoring family heirlooms to their original splendor, Tanglewood Restoration brings back the beauty of your treasured pieces.

S & L Woodcraft and Caning

6505 South 500 W
Topeka, IN 46571
260-593-0325 Ext. 1

Offering chair caning on all sizes and patterns, S & L Woodcraft and Caning works with Rush and Natural Cane and does repairs on wicker furniture.

J & S Auctions

68244 State Road 13
Millersburg, IN 46526
(574) 642-0444

Let J & S Auctions cover all your auction needs. Services include estate, antiques, real estate and personal property sells as well as real estate appraisals.

Boutiques and Consignments

FOLK ART

Emporium Flea Markets

Emporium Beech Grove 3535 South Emerson Avenue• Churchman Plaza • (317) 787-1865

Emporium 31 U.S. 31 and Declaration Drive• Greenwood • (317) 865-1865

Emporium 40 1225 South High School Road • Indianapolis • (317) 241-1865

Founded in July 2009 by Robbin and David Overbeck, the County Line Emporium, once located at County Line Road and State Road 135, was relocated to Beech Grove last year and renamed after the city. The new site provided the Overbecks with a much larger facility, which was recently enlarged by 8,000 square feet to accommodate a growing business. The Emporium was established to benefit the community, create jobs and offer a place for vendors to sell their products.

The Emporium has given many residents the opportunity to find other means of income. If offers a marketplace for anyone wanting to start a shop, but without the overhead or headaches of independently running a business.

In November 2011, David and Robbin created more jobs when opening their second store, Emporium 31, which is located at U.S. 31 and Declaration Drive, across from Kroger in Greenwood.

They opened their third location, Emporium 40, 1225 S. High School Road this summer. If you love antique malls, craft fairs, flea markets or shopping small independent vendors, you will love their stores, which feature friendly employees in clean and fun places to shop. There is something for everyone...without the huge markup in a commercial store setting. The Overbecks enjoy giving back to the community and look forward to your business.

Sell It Again, Sam!
5541 MLK Jr. Blvd • Anderson, IN • (765) 640-8991
www.sellitagainsam.us

"Sell It Again, Sam!" is locally owned and operated . We welcome you to explore our 20,000 sq. ft. showroom!

If it's interesting, unique and one-of-a-kind, then it's probably here.

We sell furniture, home and office decor, collectibles, gifts, floral designs, antique furniture, primitives, glassware, lamps, handbags, jewelry, scarves and accessories.

We receive new items daily! Booth space available.

Itty Bitty Acres
315 North Jefferson Street • Converse, IN 46919 • (574) 702-0408
www.ittybittyacres.us

Don't let the name fool you. There's nothing small about Itty Bitty Acres' vast selection of quality homemade items all at affordable prices. While this adorable shop specializes in fairy garden décor, a wide range of unique products are available including primitive-country décor, Victorian Heart, Nancy's

Nook, Candleberry Candles, Shabby Chic décor, purses and accessories. Featured on "Little Indiana," Itty Bitty Acres understands the importance of supporting the community. See all the wonderful things the store has to offer at www.facebook.com/converseittybitty, or stop by Wed. thru Sat., 10 am until 6 pm.

Jasper Gift Basket & Popcorn Company

1522 Newton Street
Jasper, IN 47546
(812) 634-2700
www.jaspergiftbasketandpopcornco.com

Beginning in 2009 as a home-based business, Jasper Gift Basket & Popcorn Company has rapidly expanded and now boasts a storefront location in the quaint German town of Jasper, Indiana. The adorable shop designs and creates the most beautiful hand-packed gift baskets in Southern Indiana. More than 90 flavors of fresh gourmet popcorn and a scrumptious selection of hand-made chocolates also have won them acclaim. Like their Facebook page to see firsthand all the goodies the shop has to offer.

The Stitching Post

401 East Main Street
Washington, IN 47501
(812) 254-6063
www.stitchingpostquilts.com

Family owned and operated, The Stitching Post, a quilting store in Washington, Indiana, started in 1986 when Mary Dell Memering purchased an existing fabric store. Over the last 27 years, Memering has transformed the store into one of Southern Indiana's largest quilting fabric suppliers. The Stitching Post offers more than 10,000 bolts of cotton fabrics from many of the nation's leading fabric designers plus a large variety of books, patterns and notions. The store prides itself as being a happy place where quilt lovers can browse at their leisure.

A 2nd Glance Consignment, LLC
1534 Main Street
Elwood, IN 46036
(765) 552-2400

You can find almost anything at A 2nd Glance Consignment LLC in Elmwood, Indiana. Owner Robin Trueblood helps buyers find good deals on name brand items including clothing for all ages, electronics, jewelry, baby items and more. Make plans to shop the savings today. Open Tuesday through Friday 11 am until 6 pm, and Saturday noon to 5 pm. Visit their Facebook page to check out some of their items currently on sale.

Sycamore Cottage
109 East Sycamore Street
Kokomo, IN 46901
(765) 868-2565

Sycamore Cottage offers a unique combination of gifts and home décor items. The shop carries American-made candles exclusive to the area such as McCall's, Tyler and Root, and Abby Candles, produced in Muncie, Indiana. A wide variety of Heritage Lace, Claire Burke and Poo-pourri candles alongside an ever-changing selection of antique items create a fun shopping experience. Open Monday thru Friday from 10 am to 6 pm and Saturday 10 am to 2 pm.

The Nest
510 East Broadway
Logansport, IN 46947
(574) 753-4444

From Yankee Candles and Vera Bradley to gifts for any occasion, shoppers will always find what they are looking for at The Nest.

Box of Chocolates
520 Vincennes Street
New Albany, IN 47150
(812) 948-2957

"You never know what your gonna get."
Upscale consignment shop with men's, women's children's clothing, housewares, jewelry, purses and shoes. Hours: Mo-Tu: 10am-6pm • Th-Fr: 10am-6pm • Sa: 10am-5 pm • Closed W & Su

Village Peddler
1828 East Broadway
Logansport, IN 46947
(574) 722-6165

Trying to find a boutique that has it all? Visit the Village Peddler, Logansport's source for all things including gifts, jewelry, baby items, handbags and more.

Martin's Quilt Shop
25387 CR 46
Nappanee, IN 46550
(574) 831-2256

Famous for hand-stitched quilts, dolls, teddy bears, and more, Martin's Quilt Shop can also create a quilt of your own design or repair treasured heirlooms.

Old Mill Flea
Market & Campground
7249 First State Highway 62
Friendship, IN 47021
(812) 667-5322
www.friendshipoldmillfleamarket.com

During the second and third weeks of June and Sept., we come alive with dealers during the National Muzzleloaders Championship Shoot.

Friendship
Flea Market
6491 E. St. Rd. 62
Versailles, IN 47042
(812) 667-5645
www.friendshipfleamarket.com
Open 2nd & 3rd full weeks of June and September (9 straight days) during the National Muzzleloaders Championship Shoot.

Amish Heritage in Northern Indiana

By Jennifer Meier

*N*orthern Indiana is not only home to the modern recreational vehicle industry; it's also the heart of the state's Amish country.

You are as likely to see the latest luxury model RV traveling down the road as you are to see an Amish family traveling by horse and buggy to one of the many local farmers' markets.

Fresh produce, locally made jams and jellies, hand-made furniture, hand-stitched quilts abound in the town of Shipshewana, located just south of the 80/90 toll road in LaGrange County.

Home to the third largest Amish and Mennonite community in the country, less than a square mile with no more than 650 residents, this tiny town of treasures attracts more than half a million visitors a year.

Folks from all over the country arrive for the weekly Wednesday antique auctions featuring a large variety of furniture, 'smalls' and specialty items. Next door to

the two spacious auction barns is the Midwest's largest open-air flea market with more then 900 vendors setting up shop each Tuesday and Wednesday from April through November.

The town also boasts more than 150 retail shops and boutiques with many one-of-kind treasures waiting to be found. On the upper floor of the Davis Mercantile, both adults and children will enjoy a step back in time with a ride on a carefully restored and colorful 1906 carousel.

To understand the rich cultural heritage and strong faith of the "plain people" visitors are welcomed into the Menno-Hof Center where they will experience the Amish and Mennonite story.

Family-style Amish meals including fried chicken, mashed potatoes, roast beef, green beans, corn, apple sauces and pies are served at many local restaurants including the Blue Gate Restaurant in the center of town, and Das Dutchman Essenhaus in the neighboring town of Middlebury.

The small town of Middlebury is home to Krider Garden, the crown jewel of the local parks and a replica of the stunning garden created for the 1933-34 Chicago World's Fair.

The two towns are linked by the ever-lengthening picturesque Pumpkinvine Trail, a product of the national Rails to Trails project that allows visitors and residents to travel by foot or bike through the colorful countryside between Shipshewana, Middlebury, Goshen and Elkhart.

Menno-Hof
See and hear the Amish-Mennonite story
510 South Van Buren Street • Shipshewana, IN 46565
(260) 768-4117 • info@mennohof.org • www.mennohof.org

Located in the heart of Amish country, Menno-Hof is a valuable first-stop before taking in the rich landscape and gentle charm of the area. Run by a non-profit organization, the center offers visitors accurate information about the faith and life of the Amish and Mennonites, both of which are part of a 500-year-old religious tradition embracing peace, simple living and Christian service.

During your visit, follow the trail of a people searching for peace as visitors step into the 16th century courtyard portraying where Anabaptism began. The tour also features a dungeon that depicts the persecution early

Anabaptists suffered for their faith. Farther along, guests board a 17th century ship on a journey to America and freedom. At the end of the visit, learn about Mennonites and Amish in modern day Indiana, experience the destructive force of nature in the tornado theatre and, finally, reflect in the calm of the meeting house.

With a gift shop that features handcrafted items made by local Amish and Mennonites, Menno-Hof is open Monday through Saturday. Visit their website for more information.

Cass County Historical Society

1004 East Market Street
Logansport, IN 46947
(574) 753-3866
www.casshistory.com

Organized in 1965, the Cass County Historical Society, Inc. was created for the purpose of discovering, collecting and preserving material which identifies and illustrates the history of this area.

The society provides for the preservation of such material and makes it accessible to the public in the Margaret Wade Archives. There it houses many county records such as probate packets, deed books and indices, court records, marriage records, tax records, etc.

The People's Winery

414 South Third Street
Logansport, IN 46947
(574) 516-1559

With a warm, inviting atmosphere, The People's Winery is the perfect place to share a bottle of wine with friends. A wide variety of wines are always available for tasting. Take your favorite home as a reminder of the special visit. The custom winery also carries locally made soy candles and jewelry, one-of-a-kind handmade wine gift bags, salsa, jams and art. Stop by and spend some down time at The People's Winery.

We welcome you to visit us on Facebook!

Hours: • Tuesday - Friday 2 p.m. - 8 p.m..
       • Saturday 11 a.m. - 7 p.m.
       • Sunday 11 a.m. - 4 p.m.

The History Center

302 East Berry Street
Fort Wayne, IN 46802
(260) 426-2882
www.fwhistorycenter.com

From Gen. Anthony Wayne to the inventor of the television, the History Center showcases Allen County history. We also invite you to visit the National Historic Landmark home of Miami Chief John Baptiste de Richardville on Bluffton Road.

Central Indiana
Historic Museums
and Venues

Indiana State Museum

By Emma Bowen Meyer

If you go:

What: Indiana State Museum

Where: 650 W. Washington Street in the heart of White River State Park in downtown Indianapolis

Hours: Monday-Saturday 10 a.m.-5 p.m. and Sunday 11 a.m.–5 p.m.

Phone: (317) 232-1637

Website: www.indianamuseum.org

Walking through the 270,000 square feet of the Indiana State Museum is akin to walking side-by-side with Hoosiers of the past. Committed to an authentic experience, curators of the majestic mirror of bygone days insist on displaying authentic artifacts to educate and delight their patrons.

"We have real genuine artifacts," said Dale Ogden, curator of cultural history. "These are not representations or models or props or photographs. These aren't things that look like or could have been handled by Abraham Lincoln or Civil War soldiers, but things that were actually owned by them."

Three floors of core galleries tell the story of the art, science and culture that has shaped the Hoosier state. No matter the interests of the patrons, an exhibit is sure to speak directly to them.

"There is a little bit for everybody," Ogden said. "Whether you like prehistoric animals that were actually discovered in Indiana, the pioneers, fine art, the military or automobiles, you will find something fascinating."

Not only does the Indiana State Museum offer natural and cultural displays for the public to enjoy, museum representatives also physically participate in paleontological digs and analyze their findings.

"What makes us unique is that we go into the field, bring specimens back, conduct analysis on them and show them to the public," said Damon Lowe, chief curator of science and biology. "Nobody else participates in the whole spectrum like that. Universities are able to do excavation and analysis but don't have the venue to display their findings to the public."

Even the impressive building itself is an exhibit of Indiana materials. Limestone, sandstone, steel, brick and glass from the Hoosier state have been crafted into a beautiful structure in the heart of White River State Park. Etched along the exterior walls are icons that represent each of the state's 92 counties.

With a simple beginning in 1862, the original collection was comprised of minerals and curiosities that state librarian R. Deloss Brown kept in a cabinet. Now more than 542,000 cultural and natural history items are counted among the collection – not to mention the presence of the state's largest IMAX theatre screen.

Displays are rotated several times a year, and special exhibits fill the halls for short durations, making the Indiana State Museum a place to visit frequently.

James Whitcomb Riley
Boyhood Home and Museum

250 West Main Street • Greenfield, IN 46140 • (317) 462-8539
www.jwrileyhome.org

Visit the world of Indiana's most well-known poet at the James Whitcomb Riley Boyhood Home and Museum in Greenfield, IN, or as Riley called it, "the best town outside of Heaven".

Born in a log cabin on the property, young James moved into the 1850 home his father built as a toddler. Here "Little Orphant Annie" came to stay, and "The Raggedy Man" worked. The museum contains original works by Riley as well as personal affects left by his family and other period pieces. Hostesses also share stories about the famous author, and even recite an occasional poem, to visitors.

As the unofficial Poet Laureate of America, Riley would go on to write more than 1,000 poems – many which were inspired by the town where he lived. In October of every year, the city celebrates his life with the Riley Festival complete with craft booths, entertainment and a poetry contest.

Both the old homestead and the museum are open for visitation from the first Tuesday of April to the last Saturday of October. During this time, hours of operation are Tuesdays through Saturdays 11 am until 4 pm.

Anderson/Madison County Visitors Bureau
6335 S. Scatterfield Road • Anderson, IN 46013

(765) 643-5633 • www.visitandersonmadisoncounty.com

From exciting Casino action to Live Horse Racing, from Historic Theatres and Beautiful Parks to ancient Great Mounds, Anderson and Madison County, Indiana is where you want to be! We also offer great sporting arenas, recreation venues and an array of lodging facilities, shopping and restaurants. Anderson/Madison County has everything you want to get your fun started!

VisitAndersonMadisonCounty.com for exciting upcoming events and plan your next visit today... **because your FUN starts here!**

Kokomo Automotive Museum

1500 North Reed Road • Kokomo, IN 46901 • (765) 454-9999
www.kokomoautomotivemuseum.org

Cruise on by the Kokomo Automotive Museum, home to more than 100 antique automobiles. Located in Kokomo, a city where some of the earliest automotive manufacturing took place, the museum proudly displays the world's largest exhibit of hometown-built Haynes and Apperson automobiles. Learn about the history of the car through a great collection of signage and other memorabilia including a 1950s diner and service station diorama. From the fabled Model T of the 1920s to the muscle cars of the 1960s, visitors of all ages are in for a thrilling ride down memory lane.

Benjamin Harrison Presidential Site

1230 North Delaware Street • Indianapolis, IN 46202 • (317) 631-1888
www.Bhpsite.org

Designated as a National Historic Landmark by the U.S. Department of the Interior, the home of America's 23rd President Benjamin Harrison continues to charm visitors as an enchanting museum. Built in 1875 by Harrison and his wife Caroline, the home went through major restoration and refurbishing in 1974 as well as a cosmetic renovation from 2006 to 2009. Ten rooms have been restored with the third floor ball room serving as an exhibition gallery. Eighty percent of the artifacts are originals, including Harrison's White House desk, a hand carved can commemorating the first 100 years of the presidency, and other furnishings used by the family on a daily basis.

Paramount Theatre

1124 Meridian Street • Anderson, IN 46016 • (765) 642-1234
www.andersonparamount.org

Built in 1929, the historic Paramount Theatre Center and Ballroom has been a landmark in downtown Anderson for more than 80 years. Designed by John Eberson as a silent movie house, the theater is home to Anderson Symphony Orchestra and Anderson Young Ballet Theatre. Restored in 1989, it remains the center of downtown, offering arts, entertainment and community events year round. The Paramount endures as one of the 12 remaining atmospheric theaters built by Eberson in the country, and is one of the three theaters in America to have its original pipe organ, which musicians still play.

The Anderson Center for the Arts

32 West 10th Street
Anderson, IN 46016
(765) 649-1248
www.andersonart.org

Beautifully restored, the 1904 Carnegie Library is an unforgettable setting when visiting the Anderson Center for the Arts. Entering through 15 foot oak doors, guests are immersed in grand style. Vaulted ceilings, marble walls, a 35 foot high rotunda with a stained glass dome, carved wood fireplaces, ornate plaster detail and gold leafing throughout provide an exquisite touch. Housing galleries of original works of art, the center is the perfect location for public and private events.

Clinton County Historical Society and Museum

301 East Clinton Street
Frankfort, IN 46041
(765) 659-2030
www.cchsm-indiana.com

Located in a beautiful Romanesque revival style sandstone building, this museum allows visitors to go back in time & experience Hoosiers' everyday turn-of-the-century lifestyle.

Rotary Jail Museum & Tannenbaum Cultural Center

225 N. Washington St.
Crawfordsville, IN 47933
765-362-5222
www.rotaryjailmuseum.org

The 1882 Rotary Jail Museum in Crawfordsville has a round cell-block built on a revolving turntable. Tours Wednesday through Saturday.

Southern Indiana
Historic Museums
and Venues

State Historical Sites

George Rogers Clark Memorial

The Red Skelton Museum

Indiana

Vincennes/Knox County Convention & Visitors Bureau

779 South 6th Street • Vincennes, IN 47591
(800) 886-6443• www.vincennescvb.org

Our showcase of historic sites include: George Rogers Clark National Historical Park, the largest federal monument outside of Washington DC; Grouseland, the mansion and museum of our 9th U.S. President, William Henry Harrison; the Vincennes State Historic Sites, including the Indiana Territory Capitol, the Jefferson Academy, Indiana's first college and the Elihu Stout Print Shop, Indiana's first newspaper publishing company; The Old Cathedral, Indiana's first church and the Old French House and Indian Museum. Further sites include the Indiana Military Museum housing one of the best comprehensive collections of military artifacts in the Midwest and the newly opened Red Skelton Museum of American Comedy, a fully interactive museum that looks at comedy through the lens of Red Skelton.

"Relive the Story" of Indiana's Territorial Past in Knox County. Vincennes is Indiana's First City and an ideal get away for history enthusiasts.

William Henry Harrison's Grouseland

3 West Scott Street • Vincennes, IN 47591 • (812) 882-2096

Grouseland, built in 1803 along the banks of the Wabash River in Vincennes, Indiana, is a visual feast and a history lover's dream. This family home of ninth U.S. president William Henry Harrison was the first brick house in the Indiana Territory, a gubernatorial mansion, and cultural and social center of the frontier. The over 20 room National Landmark features period architecture and interiors, authentic Harrison family furnishings, as well as political and military memorabilia, including the Grouseland Rifle, official gun of the state of Indiana.

Grouseland was saved from the wrecking ball by the Francis Vigo chapter of the DAR in 1909. Opened in 1911 as a house museum and has been open continuously ever since.

People come from all over to see the home and artifacts of an American President, to view period furnishings and architecture, hear about territorial history and see the native plants and restored Walnut Grove where Harrison and Shawnee Chief Tecumseh held their famous meetings.

OPEN YEAR ROUND, 7 DAYS PER WEEK (except Christmas, Thanksgiving, and New Year's) 10AM-5PM
Group tours, special programming and flexible scheduling available.
Phone: (812) 882-2096
Follow us on Facebook.
www.grouseland.org

Grouseland Foundation, stewards of the Indiana Territorial Governor's Mansion of William Henry Harrison and future US President in Vincennes, Indiana, is proud to own one of only six known remaining guns made by John Small, the first sheriff of Knox County, Indiana, at a time when Knox County extended across the current states of Indiana, Illinois, Wisconsin and Michigan.

Dubois County Museum

12704 North Newton Street • Jasper, IN 47546 • (812) 634-7733
www.duboiscountymuseum.org

History comes to life at the Dubois County Museum, one of the largest county museums in the state of Indiana. Located in the southern Indiana town of Jasper, known for its genuine Hoosier hospitality, the Dubois County Museum has more than 50,000 square feet and 7,000 objects on exhibit.

While many reflect the history of Dubois County and southern Indiana, other exhibits take you back to the time of Indian cultures, French explorers, the immigration of Irish and German settlers and early settlement lifestyles. All of life's most powerful influences including religion and education, skilled pioneer trades, the progression of farm equipment dating back to before the 1900s, military history and honored veterans, hand-painted murals and the development of the area's tremendous wood working industries are also included. Masterfully done, the exhibits will connect visitors to their forgotten past.

Remember times gone by stopping by the museum, open Tuesdays thru Fridays from 10 am until 2 pm, Saturdays from 10 am until 4 pm and Sundays from 1 to 4 pm.

West Baden Springs Hotel Atrium

Nearby, a different world

French Lick Resort is a world-class destination full of history and elegance, comfortably within reach. Two grand hotels tied to international stars of stage and screen, U.S. Presidents and infamous characters.

Four Championship Golf Courses · Two World-Class Spas
Vegas-Style Casino · Headline Entertainment
14 Dining Options · KidsFest · Conference Center

One great resort and two grand hotels.
888-936-9360 · *frenchlick.com*

French Lick Springs Hotel

West Baden Springs Hotel

FRENCH LICK RESORT

FRENCH LICK & WEST BADEN · INDIANA

FRENCH LICK SPRINGS
HOTEL

WEST BADEN SPRINGS
HOTEL

Must be 21 years or older to enter the casino. Gambling Problem? Call 1.800.9.WITH.IT!

Daviess County Chamber of Commerce and Visitors Bureau

1 Train Depot Street • Washington, IN 47501 • (812) 254-5262
www.daviesscountychamber.com

Daviess County, Indiana has a range of shops to experience. Our Amish entrepreneurs encourage you to venture our way for a visit to an authentic restaurant or take in homemade baked goods, jellies, candies, cookware, baking supplies, furniture, quilts and supplies.

Interested in Sewing and Quilting? Sprinkled throughout the rural countryside are shops with thousands of bolts of fabric and examples of the most beautiful quilts hand stitched by our local artisans. Travel the back roads and see a different way of life when you visit the buggy

shops, collar shops, auctions and greenhouses. There's even a machine shop that runs on air.

In the small towns that make up our county there are also flea markets, country shops and many specialty boutiques. Halfway between everywhere, we are an hour from Evansville, Terre Haute and Bloomington and midway between St. Louis and Cincinnati. Contact us at the Chamber and Visitors Bureau at 812-254-5262 for maps and information on how to take an Amish Tour. We invite you to slow down our way and treat yourself to Daviess County.

Bluespring Caverns Park

1459 Blue Spring Caverns Road • Bedford, IN 47421 • (812) 279-9471
www.bluespringcaverns.com

Explore the beauty and awe of some of nature's most majestic wonders at Bluespring Caverns Park in Bedford, Indiana. Take a memorable journey on the Mys'try River Voyage, an hour long boat tour along Indiana's longest underground river. Formed over thousands of years, the caverns support many kinds of wildlife including a large population of rare blind fish. Other amenities include park facilities, gemstoneing, a nature trail and a gift shop. Open everyday March 16 to October 31.

Bubble Gum Bed and Breakfast

517 W. Ohio Street • Rockville, IN 47872 • (765) 569-6630

Visit historic Bubble Gum Bed and Breakfast in Rockville, IN; home of the Covered Bridge Festival. Built in 1909, relax in one of the 3 bedrooms; Hope, Love or Faith and enjoy a full country breakfast. Dream of days gone by with bubble gum and chocolate on the beautiful enclosed porch. Reservations required.

Pike County Chamber of Commerce

714 East Main Street
Petersburg, IN 47567
(812) 354-8155
www.pikecountyin.org

"Pick your Way" to Pike County. Treasures abound in the southern Indiana county with fantastic antique and craft shopping, beautiful scenery and delicious dining. Relax and enjoy the Hoosier hospitality of friendly and knowledge proprietors as you search for your own little piece of history.

Vintage automobiles also take center stage in Pike. Every year, the county hosts two major antique car shows.

Visit the Chamber website for a calendar of events and more detailed information.

Cherrywood Farm Bed and Breakfast

8184 South 625 West
Rosedale, IN 47874
(765) 548-0582
www.cherrywoodfarm.com

Relax on the 72 quiet, wooded acres of Cherrywood Farm. Located in Parke County, home to some of the state's most lovely covered bridges, the 1863 farmhouse has been restored to original detail when possible. Choose from three beautiful bedrooms, all with private baths and a full breakfast. Nearby at the working orchard, pick some of the freshest fruit in the region including strawberries, blueberries, and blackberries available. Open March through November.

Daviess County Historical Society Museum

212 East Main Street
Downtown Washington
(812) 257- 0301 / (812) 444-9360
Hours: Tuesday-Saturday noon to 5 p.m. or by appointment

Batesville Area Chamber of Commerce & Visitor Center

16 East George Street
Batesville, IN 47006
(812) 934-3101
www.batesvillein.com

Explore an 1865 historic inn, a micro-brewery, a world-renowned woodcarving shop, an art gallery, antiques shops and much, much more.

Visit Madison

601 West First Street
Madison, IN 47250
(800) 259-2956
www.visitmadison.org

Nestled along the Ohio River in Southern Indiana, Madison is truly a quaint "river town" offering antique and specialty stores, bed and breakfasts, historical tours and plenty of other activities and events.

Ripley County Tourism Bureau and Welcome Center

220 East US 50
Versailles, IN 47042
(800) 747-5394
www.ripleycountytourism.com

Learn about all the area has to offer including the Milan 54 Hoosiers Museum, Versailles State Park and much more.

T

U/V

W

X,Y,Z

Published by Pediment Publishing, a division of The Pediment Group, Inc. www.pediment.com

Design by Stephen Allen, Tim Bath, Stefani Closson, Amy Newcom, Rodney Ogle, Bev Sams

ISBN-13: 978-1-59725-475-5

To order copies of this book, please contact CNHI Indiana Media Group
Bev Sams
300 North Union Street
Kokomo, IN 46901
(765) 854-6707